Healthy ways to *Work* in *Health Care*

a self care guide

25 TIPS FOR FINDING AND ENRICHING YOUR LIFE'S WORK

FOREWORDS BY: TERRY WEINBURGER, *SCL HEALTH SYSTEM*
THOMAS MOORE, BEST SELLING AUTHOR, *CARE OF THE SOUL IN MEDICINE*

Martin Helldorter, MS, MA, D.MIN. *with* Terri Moss

Moss Communications
Orinda, CA 94563
Tel: (925)377-5288
www.mosscommunications.net
terri@mosscommunications.net

Ordering information:
Special discounts are available for group purchases.
Please contact Moss Communications or go to our website for more information.

Printed in Canada by Spectrum Books and Friesen's Corporation

Moss Communications books are printed using paper that has been manufactured by environmentally responsible processes, when available. This may include using trees grown in sustainable forests and incorporating recycled paper.

Book design by Nicole Watson, Pensé Design (415) 456-6262, San Rafael, CA
www.pensedesign.com

Library of Congress Cataloguing-in-Publication Data
Helldorfer, Martin
Moss, Terri
Healthy Ways to Work in Health Care: A Self Care Guide
by Martin Helldorfer and Terri Moss

p. cm.
ISBN-978-0-9833014-3-1

"Health care is one of the few professions where ignoring your spouse, significant other, friends, family, yourself for that matter, is still socially acceptable."

ROBERT WICKS, PHD, LOYOLA UNIVERSITY

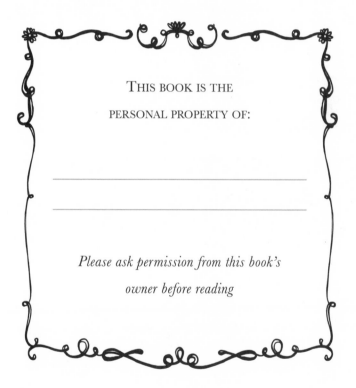

THIS BOOK IS THE
PERSONAL PROPERTY OF:

_____

_____

*Please ask permission from this book's
owner before reading*

Dedication

Sister Peggy Egan, O.S.F., Ph.D.

*As an executive and educator, you have taught us what
it means to work with passion and love for those we serve.
As Clare and Francis of Assisi have shaped your life,
so you have shaped mine. Thank you.*

Contents

Foreword

by Thomas Moore, Best Selling Author, Care of the Soul, and Care of the Soul in Medicine

*In this wise, subtle and penetrating book, Martin Helldorfer and Terri Moss
tease out the important questions and offer ways of dealing with our own sickness
and taking care of others that go far beyond the physical. It's not often that
I feel confident in the psychological help offered to the sick and their families,
but this book is truly trustworthy and useful.*

A few years ago I was speaking to a group of doctors on the faculty of the school of medicine at McGill University. One doctor made a comment that has stayed with me: "Sometimes, when I turn my back, the patient gets better." She wasn't putting down her skills or efforts; she was acknowledging the mysterious aspects of healing. Things happen in spite of our knowledge and treatments.

In our high-tech, information driven and evidence-based world, I'm out of place. I have a doctorate in religious studies and approach illness and healing full of images from the spiritual traditions. I always remember Jesus healing with words and touch, the Medicine Buddha brilliant in his blue body, Quan Yin holding her vial of ointment and backing off a fierce dragon. I think, too, of St. Sebastian, patron of medicine, martyred by being shot through with arrows—an early wounded healer. I think of Native American medicine men and women decked out in outrageously flashing feathers and beads, and the Siberian shamans with their drums that sound the rhythms of life and death.

Illness is not just a physical malady. A patient's emotions and sense of meaning, his soul and spirit, his family and friends, his world and work are all implicated in the illness and therefore have a role in his healing. Where did this illness come from, anyway? Why not someone else? Why not some other time? Why not some other symptoms?

In speaking of the mystery of illness and healing to doctors, sometimes I meet strong resistance. In the spirit of our times, they see illness as a problem to be solved. And so they focus their attention on their knowledge, on the body of research and on their instruments and skills. I can't say enough how deeply this modern philosophy or mythology of fact and technology has affected the medical profession. It goes deep beyond measure, and yet for all its benefits, it can be a dangerous thing. It can take the soul out of a patient and his family, and out of the health care provider as well. I believe that morale problems common in the medical professions these days are largely due to the materialistic myth that dominates, a myth that has little room for deep human emotion and reflection, or for mystery.

The modern medical provider occasionally has to turn her back, get out of the way, so healing can commence. I often teach psychiatrists and other health care providers traditional Buddhist healing vows. The main one: Heal with your presence. Any patient can tell you how important it is to their healing for them to know who their doctor, nurse or other attendant is as a person. Doctors—and nurses now more commonly—apparently don't realize that who they are is as important as what they do with a patient. They don't seem to understand, too, the importance of a medical center or hospital being a healing community. Working together with a sense of common purpose and connection, dealing effectively with stresses and conflicts and creating a genuine air of friendship all contribute to the healing of patients.

The Greeks of old had a profound notion of illness and healing. They honored two deities, often showing them working together, each connected to the snake that still remains the symbol of medicine and is an image for the mystery I'm advocating. They are Asklepios and Hygiene, the god of healing and the goddess of health. I thought of these two when I first read the title of this remarkable book: *Healthy Ways to Work in Health Care*.

We need health as well as healing. We need a social and physical environment that is healthy in every respect: clean, quiet, friendly, beautiful and effective. We need people in touch with the inspiration that brought them mysteriously into their profession. We need an acknowledgement that life is mysterious. It has meaningful secrets, nowhere as powerfully as in the process of getting sick and getting better.

I'm encouraged and honored to have a small role in this book that with such finesse explores the details of providing health care and of supporting the men and women who give so much of their lives to the work of healing. The recommendations here are more perceptive and deeply grounded than you will find in most books designed for health care workers. I wish I could make my obscure thoughts as clear and applicable as this book does. Here you have a sourcebook that you can turn to daily for inspiration and guidance, and that in itself is a kind of healing.

When we talk about the whole person in medicine, we should be talking about both patients and providers. One whole person evokes health and healing for a patient who is a whole person. So, give this valuable book with confidence to anyone in the health professions. Write a note in it encouraging him or her in their deep-seated calling and suggest that they keep the book close at hand, maybe on the job. One thing is true about soul and spirit: they are easily forgotten, especially in a high-tech environment.

To be a healer you don't have to be in perfect condition whether physically, emotionally or spiritually. But you need to be in the process of healing yourself. That's how it works. As you heal, your patient gets better. As your patient heals, you get better. Read this book closely and more than once. It has the capacity to heal you.

Foreword

by Terry Weinburger, Senior Vice President, Mission Integration SCL Health System

How many of us in health care dare to think of our work as a way to build a better world? Specifically how many health care professionals passionately believe they can make a difference in their daily work? After fifty plus years of actively listening to patients, clients, and the health care professionals, Martin Helldorfer offers us his self care guide to enrich our work life and build a better world. We have been given a gift!

Helldorfer is a master storyteller who harvested vignettes from his life experience of listening and being fully present in the moment with others. Plunging headlong, heart-felt and spirit-filled into storytelling, Helldorfer offers us practical tools to live by, to improve our career satisfaction and increase our team functioning; as a result, we can deepen our person-centered care. His health care stories focus on the fundamental predicament of our human condition, offering us real life people who face the daily challenge of staying intact body, mind and spirit as they daily stand on the abyss of pain, suffering, emergent new life and pending death. Tips, case studies and inspirational reflections are sprinkled throughout the book providing substantive nourishment—a careful reflective reading will help us all burn brightly without burning out.

The unhealthy ways we work—fixation, addiction and exhaustion—are exposed as characteristics of over work. In his gentle and persuasive style, Helldorfer invites us to clarify our attitudes toward work while deepening the conversation through the lens of self-reflection. He encourages us to reflect on our own self care. To enjoy a balanced life he suggests it "might be as much a state of mind as a physical apportionment of time."

You will be challenged to put your cards on the table face up, if you read, reflect and take time to journal as you are reading. Also readers will appreciate the insights gleaned in the process of this "deep dive." Helldorfer then helps us journey toward re-imagining, re-inventing, and re-sculpting ourselves and our careers.

Each chapter is a blend of theological, spiritual and contemporary meanings that will resonate with and enliven our spirits! Helldorfer's ideas, attitudes, and insights offer us all a repository of practical resources. Helldorfer offers us social glue that brings us all together around the common value of compassion. Through his storytelling we come to realize that our value as individuals transcends our ability to do things. His self care guide offers us a critical pathway that informs our thinking and then transforms us toward a more holistic model of living an engaged, joy-filled life. Our times and health care settings beckon for this renewal.

For health care providers, this is another lodestar from Helldorfer who is at his vintage best—a sage who gives us a guide to living a more balanced life in our fast-paced, high tech, high touch environment. His book has lasting insights that are time-honored but nuanced for the 21st century calling forth the promise within us to live a more authentic life.

Reviews

*"**Healthy Ways to Work in Health Care: A Self Care Guide** is a wonderful companion piece to **Healing with Heart: Inspirations for Health Care Professionals**, also by Martin Helldorfer and Terri Moss. What a gift this book is to those who spend their lives caring for others, often at great personal cost. Generally, health care workers are externally focused, overlooking personal discomfort in order to provide care to another. What we forget is that self care is a pre-requisite to caring for others, and if not addressed, it can lead to compassion fatigue and burnout. It is impossible to give from a state of depletion. **Healthy Ways to Work in Health Care: A Self Care Guide** provides the tools and dialogue that nurture and sustain all caregivers.*

The introspective approach and the use of reflective journaling allow the health care worker to make this journey about them, allowing them the opportunity to heal and regain the joy they once had when they started in their chosen profession.

The exercises are useful not only for an individual but also for groups. I can envision this work assisting with team building and focusing the energy of the team. With all of the distractions in the health care environment, the ability to focus on what is most important is essential."

ANNE M. FOSS-DURANT, RN, MN, FNP, MBA
NURSE LEADER, *NORTHERN CALIFORNIA, CARITAS COACH*

ℰ

"Martin invites the reader to take a reflective walkabout the territory of self in the complex system of health care. Yes, health care is about the patient. And Martin reminds us that the compassionate care of the patient is best delivered by the provider who is both aware of themselves and their relationship to work.

With the collective wisdom of relevant stories, thought–provoking questions and a lens to understanding one's self at work, **Healthy Ways to Work in Health Care: A Self Care Guide** is a gift to providers and patients alike. This book is essential reading for any caregiver in health care who wants to balance their care-receiving with a deeper appreciation of who they are in both their being and doing. Share this book liberally with others."

KEVIN BUCK, PRINCIPAL, *EMERGENT SUCCESS INC.* "WORKING BETTER - TOGETHER."

ॐ

"The challenge of achieving work-life balance is a hot topic among health care practitioners. Everyone seems to agree on its importance, but the conversation often reverts to the inherent stresses in health care work and the impossibility of ever doing anything to correct it. Futility has reigned supreme…until now!

With this publication, Marty Helldorfer and Terri Moss not only provide a clear analysis of the problem's multiple facets, but they also outline steps everyone can take to stop self-defeating behaviors, understand their own causative factors, and begin the process of healing themselves and their workplace environment.

Content organization is very effective. The insights into various aspects influencing work-life balance are presented with clarity and a fresh approach to self-understanding as the basis for healing from within. The current stresses and pressure faced by nurses and other practitioners provides a context that projects an unmistakable authenticity of understanding the real world of health care today. Many chapters include case studies, practical 'tips' and reflective questions to deepen the reader's understanding and application of the content provided.

I found every aspect of this book to accurately describe this difficult and complex problem, based on my own experiences and insights. The best part is the new insights into who we are and how that impacts work-life balance. And the best news is that the authors have provided a useful and practical pathway into work-life balance. I especially approve of their recommendation about how to handle having more work to do than time available! This book provides solutions for this very perplexing reality of work-life imbalance."

MARIE MANTHEY, FOUNDER AND PRESIDENT EMERITIS,
CREATIVE HEALTH CARE MANAGEMENT

❧

*"As a physician, patient, and cancer survivor, I echo the authors' admiration of dedicated health care professionals who make a daily difference in patients' and families' lives. What makes **Healthy Ways to Work in Health Care: A Self Care Guide** distinctive is its focus on the inner journey, based on understanding what calls us to serve, releasing the past, being engaged in the present, and being part of a cause larger than ourselves.*

I found it affirming in Chapter 8 "Finding the Right Work" that others beside me still feel that health care is a calling. Three insights emerge:

1. *If we heed what life asks of us, a sense of peace and well-being follow.*

2. *We become more comfortable in the realization that life is an unfinished journey.*

3. *Every occupation provides people with opportunities to discover their value. I know many health care professionals, myself included, who threw themselves into their work only to lament later, "The hospital does not love me back." My only regret is that **Healthy Ways to Work in Health Care: A Self Care Guide** was not mandatory reading decades ago during my surgical residency.*

KENNETH H. COHN, MD, MBA, FACS, CEO OF *HEALTH CARE COLLABORATION* AND
AUTHOR OF *BETTER COMMUNICATION FOR BETTER CARE*,
COLLABORATE FOR SUCCESS!, AND *GETTING IT DONE*.

❧

Introduction

"A man who as a physical being is always turned toward the outside, thinking that his happiness lies outside him, finally turns inward and discovers that the source is within him."

SOREN KIERKEGAARD

This book originated nearly 30 years ago when my clinical practice primarily consisted of helping two groups of clients, all professionals: some who were hospitalized with severe mental illnesses and others whom I saw as outpatients in private practice. *Healthy Ways to Work in Health Care: A Self Care Guide* reflects what I learned from my outpatient clients—these gifted individuals who were teachers, nurses, counselors, business professionals and ministers. For almost all of them, it was only a matter of time before they reflected on the role that work played in their lives.

Given how much of my clients' waking lives were spent working, it wasn't surprising that work shaped their relationships with family and friends and deeply influenced how they felt about themselves. Some thought that the way they worked contributed to their divorces. From others, I learned that being on the job was the activity that held together their otherwise chaotic lives. A surprising number felt they were mismatched to their jobs and that if only they could find the right job, contentment would follow. Some felt trapped in a job that provided great benefits; their mindset was, "I'm unhappy, but I'd be crazy to change jobs at this time in my life." Many of my clients seemed to push themselves along as they waited for retirement.

Over the years, I began to intuit patterns and connections woven into clients' diverse stories. I sought supervision from more experienced colleagues and continually spoke with them about these patterns and connections. Little by little, hardly aware of what I was doing, I started to let go of traditional thinking about work and listened to what my clients were teaching me. That's when I coined the term "work fixation," which I could see was different from overwork, work addiction, and work exhaustion. At the same time, I was discovering the value of journal writing as a way to help patients learn about themselves—particularly how to find meaningful work and work in healthier ways.

My own career evolved and I spent years in administrative positions within large health care systems. Naturally, I became intimately involved in the daily experiences of health care professionals—the crises, the joys, the business pressures, team conflicts, and interpersonal issues they face—and appreciative of the extreme emotional, spiritual and physical balancing act they perform personally and professionally as they engage in this most important work of caring for others. Eventually my thoughts coalesced into this book, which has taken the shape of a hands-on guide for health care professionals and those who, as a result of life circumstances, are caregivers.

Healthy Ways to Work in Health Care starts by taking a step back to define work as a way to build a better world. Whether we work as nurses, physicians, astronomers, lawyers, teachers, sales people, construction workers, or parents, we're engaged in transforming the world as we know it. Even people who operate machines in a garment factory, repair flat tires, teach children to read, act on Broadway, and ferry passengers across the country are engaged in the drama of creation.

In part because of our cultural shaping as well as the demands of work and family, most of us live as if *doing* is the most important side of our life. What we forget is that the other side of doing is *being*. The two are inseparable. When we emphasize and balance being with doing, we are acknowledging that *how* we are present is as critical (or some would say more critical) than whatever it is we are doing. Nowhere is this more evident than in caregiving since our primary focus is on the people we are serving.

We are not just doers stocking grocery shelves, programming computers, running spreadsheets or repairing machinery. As health care professionals, our jobs focus on healing people and because of that, work holds some unique factors: the importance of being present in our work, that presence is influenced by our personal lives and experience, a sense of being called to our profession, the pull of this commitment, the pressures resulting from the business of health care and the immense honor and sometimes burden of caring for others. All of these factors and many more life experiences shape the worker we are and the work that we do. Imagine two nursing school professors. One is a nurse. Will being a nurse influence the way she teaches? I think so. Every experience we have in life influences how we work. You'll learn more about this in the pages that follow.

Florence Nightingale thought of nursing as a calling that requires total commitment. Her ability to be present to others was legendary. A reporter who witnessed her going about a hospital wrote in *The London Times*:

"She is a "ministering angel" without any exaggeration in these hospitals, and as her slender form glides quietly along each corridor, every poor fellow's face softens with gratitude at the sight of her. When all the medical officers have retired for the night and silence and darkness have settled down upon those miles of prostrate sick, she may be observed alone, with a little lamp in her hand, making her solitary rounds."[2]

Was the reporter exaggerating or sentimentally idealizing Nightingale's dedication, healing presence, and influence on patients? Not likely. She was a determined and focused woman who combined a tough, no-nonsense approach to improving patient care with an admired and tempered human presence that itself was healing.

Anyone who has received nursing care in a hospital, physician office, treatment center, nursing home, home health agency, or hospice knows its value. Some nurses work at the bedside, others as managers, statisticians, professors, researchers, or policy-makers. I once heard a recruiter at a job fair tell a candidate, "If you don't know what to do, get a nursing degree. You can't go wrong." Nurses do many things well. For that reason alone, they deserve our gratitude.

But, if nursing is such a valued profession, why do nurses complain sometimes about being under-appreciated and over-worked? Why do nurses joke among themselves that they can't wait to win the lottery so they'll no longer need to work? Why are some nurses always on the lookout for work situations that are more enjoyable or better paid?

Like people in other professions, nurses think a job, department, or hospital elsewhere will better suit them. Such restlessness is a good thing in many ways, as discontent can lead to a refreshed life and innovation. However, it's also true that geographical cures seldom work. Something else is necessary. The following pages explain that "something."

Many caregivers are not nurses. We typically think of physicians, pharmacists, home health aides, phlebotomists, psychologists, family therapists, surgery techs, and case managers as caregivers. But what about those who clean rooms, serve meals, and manage the heating and air conditioning at sprawling health care facilities? Or, how do information technology services employees or those working in the business side of health care influence patient care? Even though these employees may be far removed from direct patient care, they nevertheless make a palpable contribution to such care. One could say it takes a village to provide quality health care.

Who Will Benefit *from* This Book?

This book is for nurses who want to rekindle the spirit that first attracted them to the profession and know it's time to do some personal soul searching. It is not for those who are content with the way things are or who view their work as merely a job. The book can also help two other groups: health care professionals who don't have a problem with work but want to understand those who do, and workers who feel that their energies have waned.

Other important caregivers, whose numbers are legion and far exceed those of salaried workers, are the family members, friends, and neighbors who try to balance caring for chronically ill relatives, sick children, and aging parents with the other demands of family, work, and personal needs. This book is for caregivers of every stripe. While this book references the lives and experiences of health care professionals, the information and tips offered will help anyone who is feeling unsettled and is seeking more meaning from their work.

Some will want to take this journey alone, away from work. Others who are fortunate to be working with high-functioning teams where trust and respect are engrained values, will want to explore these questions with their team. However, do not expect to find a guide on how to form these high-functioning teams or how to transform organizations. Other books cover those topics.

How *to* Use *this* Book — On Your Own

These pages contain many practical suggestions on how to care for oneself while caring for others. Their purpose is to awaken insight, not solve a problem. Once you understand the factors that contribute to unhealthy work styles and behaviors, you'll know what to do. However, corrective action will differ from person to person. Singer Billie Holiday got it right when she said, "If I'm going to sing like someone else, then I don't need to sing at all."[3] What's necessary is the courage to be yourself and to make choices based on your needs.

Many of the suggestions involve journal writing, which may be surprising, as adult learning generally involves team activity and sharing insights in safe settings. This book is for people who have profited from such sessions but know they need something more at this point in their lives. Here's how one nurse put it:

"I've gone through many training and educational experiences for which I'm grateful. In spite of these many training experiences, I probably learned the most by leading the effort to get magnet status for our hospital. Even with all of this training, I know I need to draw apart as it were, maybe even turn inward, to focus on what I need to do for myself. The kinds of things I struggle with in my journal are highly personal. It would not have been appropriate to do that soul searching in a group or with colleagues."

This book offers space to jot down one's thoughts after each case study and at the end of each chapter. More journaling pages are in back of the book for further reflective writing.

The Watson Caring Science Institute (WCSI) and Creative Health Care Management (CHCM) help health care professionals, particularly nurses, recognize the critical role of presence in the healing process. Readers familiar with WCSI's and CHCM's work know that when professionals care for themselves, team performance is strengthened and the care of patients and their families enhanced. The question is how to sustain self care. The answer is reflection, time apart, and insight.

How *to* Use *this* Book—In Teams

High-functioning organizations invest in continual training for their employees, especially training that improves patient care and employee satisfaction. Hospitals that pursue ANCC Magnet status, the numerous programs offered by the Institute for Healthcare Improvement, the WCSI and CHCM programs, and the Joint Commission's education programs provide their staff with exceptional educational opportunities. The natural outcomes of many of these are personal development and self awareness.

While the journey of self awareness is often a solo adventure, the information contained in this book along with the tips, case studies, and inspirational reflections are designed also to be used in a team meeting or retreat setting to support awareness (at a personal and team level), promote team connection, and unleash the benefits of shared team learning.

Improving patient care—both clinical outcomes and patients' satisfaction with their care—requires the transformation of health care organizations. That remaking involves remarkable leadership, uncommon management skills, and teamwork. While we cannot care for others without caring for ourselves, the fact is that to improve patient care, we must be willing to let our needs as caregivers recede in importance—not forget our needs, but place them gently in the background until we can give them the full attention they deserve.

This book is about remembering the delicate task of nurturing the inward lives of dedicated and engaged caregivers. It is written for those who feel the need to reflect and think about themselves while also being present to care for others. This book will appeal to health care professionals who understand the importance of presence and are ready to ask themselves these questions: Is this what I want to do? Am I caring for myself? What is being asked of me at this time in my life?

The goal of this book is to help individuals be faithful to themselves as they care for others.

The 25 Tips in this book encourage the reader to take action. The journey inward to help yourself ultimately leads outward toward bringing a healing presence to patients.

We welcome your feedback. Please take a moment to visit us at www.mosscommunications.net.

A Reflection

A PATIENT PERSPECTIVE

Those who choose to work as caregivers are a generous lot. Their accent is on the care of others, not themselves. There is something troubling, even abhorrent, if caregivers place their needs before their patients' needs. Those who have worked within patient care settings have experienced the many personal rewards.

Last week, I watched 30 caregivers receive a remarkable gift. It was at a retreat for clinicians focused on how to improve patients' satisfaction with their care. Their hospital's HCAHPS scores were low and nothing the staff did moved them higher.

To help the clinicians assess their situation and identify solutions, the staff invited three former patients to speak to them. The plan was to have the 30 participants break into smaller groups of 10 and then have the former patients move from one group to another to describe their hospitalization experience.

The staff was noticeably on edge before the patients came into the room. Evidently many had been caregivers of these three patients. Aware of the anxiety in the room, the leader reiterated that we were there to learn. If patients were critical, we would have to quiet any inclination to explain away, deny, or contradict their experience.

The discussions that followed lasted almost two hours. Were the patients critical? You bet. Were they also appreciative? Incredibly so. There was something about being face-to-face in a safe setting that led both patients and caregivers to understand rather than blame one another.

As their time together wound down, the retreat leader asked the patients if they had a final word to the caregivers. Here is what they said:

PATIENT 1: I'm leaving here recognizing that you are not taking care of yourselves. I can now see that when you were cold and snippy it was largely because you were tired. If I could make one suggestion, it would be to take better care of yourselves. If you did, you wouldn't be so bothered by our complaints. As if by magic, your patient satisfaction scores would rise.

PATIENT 2: I don't think you know how important this place is for those of us who have been here. As critical as I have been, I love this place. On more than one occasion when I've driven by, I've said a prayer for those of you who work here. I count on you being here. I'm not alone in feeling as I do.

PATIENT 3: Today, I've been your biggest critic. I'm the one who went off at the mouth about the food, your inane rules, and your lack of communication. While you may find it hard to believe, I love you. Just remember that when you get back to work tomorrow.

It was striking to witness how the former patients ended the day ministering to the caregivers. Two of them even used the word love to describe their sentiments. Are the patients saying something that we need to hear?

As if by magic, would our patient satisfaction scores rise if we took care of ourselves? Could it be that simple? If caring for ourselves isn't entirely the key influencer of patient satisfaction, is it partially so?

The retreat was limited to thirty employees within an organization employing almost 1,500. They heard that they were appreciated, even loved. That was an unexpected gift received on a day they expected to be criticized. Given the pace and intensity of working in a hospital or nursing home, do you think that the words *appreciated* and *loved* are easy to forget? Do you think that those thirty employees were energized when they returned to work? Will the memory linger? Will patient satisfaction scores improve? ♥

To Care *for* Oneself:
Work-life Balance

"Life is like riding a bicycle. To keep
your balance you must keep moving."
ALBERT EINSTEIN

What does it mean to "care for oneself?" Does someone who
loves her job and works every day of the week, including weekends, care for herself? Is it reasonable to expect a physician to
live a "balanced life" when she works a 60-hour week and is on
call 24/7? What does it mean to live a balanced life? It may not
be a simple matter of equally portioning out eight hours of
sleep, eight hours for a personal life, and eight hours for work.
Living a balanced life might be as much a state of mind as a
physical apportionment of time.

Are those who work in health care settings expected to
dedicate themselves to caring for their patients even if it results
in their own physical or emotional exhaustion? Are health

care providers expected to work longer hours than people in other professions?

Let's look at some examples of people who are passionate about their work. Consider how you would determine if they are caring for themselves or living a balanced life. Reflect on a deeper definition of "self care" and what it means to live a balanced life.

Does this well-known maestro care for himself? He clearly loves what he does:

REPORTER: "I heard someone say you work seven days a week. Is that true?"

CONDUCTOR: "Yes, that's the case."

REPORTER: "Why do you do that?"

CONDUCTOR: "Because that's all the days there are."

How about the lab technician who, five days a week, arrives at work at 9 a.m. and leaves exactly at 5 p.m. so he can get to the gym before going home for dinner? Do his daily work-outs indicate that he cares for himself?

Can a working mother of three preschool youngsters have time to care for herself?

Before answering these questions, we need to clarify what we mean by "balance." The answers will vary depending on a person's health, personality, temperament, responsibilities, and situation.

When we think about the need to care for ourselves by living a balanced life, we probably envision an old-fashioned scale. The scale is balanced when the beam holds equal weights on both ends and imbalanced when one arm of the beam is heavier than the other. In this analogy for explaining the desire to take care of ourselves, work is usually on one arm of the scale and the remainder of life on the other. The challenge is to find ways to balance the two.

A Reflection

BALANCE

I'm in the Dallas airport with a three-and-a-half-hour layover waiting for a flight to take me to a meeting in Minneapolis. There's a group immediately across from me waiting for the same flight—three couples, four children, and two infants. For comfort and to entertain the children, everyone is sitting on the carpeted floor. The group seems more like a happy tribe than families headed by young affluent professionals.

"It's been wonderful," one of the mothers says, "but I miss my own kitchen. It's hard to relax in someone else's home even though it was fun being in Orlando with the kids."

Two of the men shake their heads in unison. One says, "I never thought I'd say it, but I'll be happy to get back to work."

Vacationers like these are pulled from their homes by the excitement of getting away. Patients may be pulled away by illness. In the airport, I started to think about those of us in health care. Caring for others can pull us to the point where we, too, want to return home—not to a place, but to ourselves. Who among us has not felt so scattered or overwhelmed that she craves just a minute or two of quiet?

It's easy for health care professionals to get pulled away from themselves and their personal needs by patients' needs, the demands of time, the expectations of others, and the demands we place on ourselves. In fact, there's always more work than enough time to do it. Generous caregivers can easily lose their balance. ♥

If you're trying to find balance in your life so you will have time to care for yourself, you're not alone. More than 51 million people have Googled the phrase "work-life balance." There are more than 9,000 printed books offering advice on this subject and more than 6,900 offering advice on "self care." Of these 6,900 books, 570 address special issues facing women, 160 focus on the challenges facing nurses, 150 are for physicians, and 49 are for social workers. The number of such books continues to swell. Many of them suggest that work-life balance and self care are a matter of time management. They advocate limiting the amount of time spent working so there will be free time for other activities, such as loving relationships, play, and exercise.

David Whyte, the philosopher-poet, thinks otherwise. He believes that attempting to achieve life balance through time management is too simplistic. Instead of thinking of it as a time-management exercise, he writes about the need to live more reflectively and honor three fundamental commitments: to ourselves, our loved ones, and our work. To accentuate the need to be faithful to each, Whyte calls the three commitments "marriages."[1] The marriages are also sacrosanct; overvaluing or disregarding one at the expense of the others is to risk trouble, as subsequent chapters in this book will make clear.

For example, a distorted commitment to work can destroy a love relationship. By focusing exclusively on work, we ignore our significant other's need for intimacy and connection, and the relationship deteriorates. Conversely, over-investing in a love relationship can destroy our work. We're so distracted by that relationship that our commitment to the demands of work and to fulfilling the job requirements is diminished and we fail. Equally unfortunate is when love relationships and work lead individuals to overlook their own needs. People who direct all of their energy, attention, love, and time to relationships and work wake up one day and find themselves physically, emotionally, and spiritually depleted. They are spent, sometimes become physically ill or run down, and have nothing left to give.

Then again, you might ask: What's the big deal about overlooking any of the three marriages? Sometimes we must be selfless and devote our lives to work if it means accomplishing a significant project. And what's so tragic about putting loved ones ahead of work or career? Nothing. We're not talking about right or wrong; rather, we're referring to what happens when one marriage outweighs another and to the problems that arise when we ignore our basic human needs.

The award-winning author Thomas Moore has a third perspective. Instead of trying to care for ourselves by pursuing a balanced life, he suggests living a "soulful" life. The distinction is more than cosmetic, as he explained in *Care of the Soul*:

A soulful life is one of thoughtfulness, care, and engagement—you are present in everything you do, not just going through the motions. You give attention to the things that matter most. You take care of your body and your health. You make your home a place of comfort, welcome, and beauty. You educate yourself throughout your life in values and solid ideas. Your leisure time relaxes you, gives you a rich social life, and provides fun and play. Your spirituality is deep as well as visionary, and you incorporate contemplation, discussion, ritual, and prayer into everyday life, and you do all of this in a style that suits you as an individual.[2]

The question is, how can we possibly live a soulful life in today's world? Viktor Frankl, the world-famous philosopher and author, has yet another perspective. He's suspicious of people who are preoccupied with caring for themselves or who want to live a balanced life if, by "balance," they mean a life without tension: "I consider it a dangerous misconception of mental hygiene to assume that what [we] need in the first place is equilibrium…What [we] actually need is to strive and struggle toward a worthy goal."[3] He maintains that what we need isn't discharge of tension at any cost, but the call of a potential meaning waiting to be fulfilled.

Frankl arrived at this belief during World War II while suffering immeasurably in a Nazi concentration camp, where he was inhumanely stripped of his possessions, identity, autonomy, and dignity. He realized how our expectations of the future shape our present moment: "Woe to him who saw no more sense in his life, no aim, no purpose, and therefore no point in carrying on. Those who felt that they had nothing to expect from life were lost."[4] Frankl called this hoped-for future one's "vocation"— something even more important than the basic human needs of dignity, identity, autonomy, pleasure, power, and possessions.

Whyte's, Moore's, and Frankl's views are key to understanding what's necessary in caring for ourselves as we care for others. Among the fundamental issues they address are what we value, the responsibilities we bear, what is asked of us in life, and how we choose to spend the commodity of time.

Before addressing these topics, we must dig a little deeper into our relationship with work—why and how we learned to work the way we do and the underlying factors that affect the role work plays in our lives. This is critically important because we cannot change distorted ways of working until we become aware of the influences that have shaped the way we work.

Case Study*

"You ask if there was an unforgettable moment that changed the way I do things. Yes. It was almost five years ago when I arrived at work and my manager asked if I could take her place at an important off-campus meeting. Unexpectedly, she couldn't go.

"'We have to have someone there,' she said. 'It's about this year's budget. We'll regret it if someone from our department isn't there.' Without a moment's hesitation, I said, 'Sure.'

"Moments later, my husband called. He told me that the school nurse had called to say that our eight year old was sick and we should pick her up immediately.

"At first, I didn't know what to do. I had just told my manager that I would go to the meeting. Should I call my husband and ask him to go? I also felt other pressures. I had a paper due that evening for a class I was taking and I was counting on completing it after I left work at 3 p.m. On top of it all, it was my responsibility during the day to call all of the volunteer blood donors scheduled for the next day. If I didn't make those calls, chances were that some of them wouldn't show up, and we needed the platelets.

"Without much thought, I asked the manager if I could go home to pick up my child. That's the day I learned that fear of displeasing others, feeling that I was not a very responsible person, and that following a to-do list too doggedly are all stumbling blocks. I now try to avoid them. That day really has changed the way I work."

LESSON: Become aware of the stumbling blocks that hinder you from putting first things first.

*The case studies in this book reflect real-life experiences of caregivers in various settings. To safeguard individuals' privacy, names have been changed. These scenarios aim to stimulate thinking and group discussion, which, in addition to fostering a lively, provocative exchange of ideas, hopefully will enable participants to get to know one another a little better. With familiarity comes the trust and team building that lead to better patient care.

A Reflection

LIFESTYLE

The Op Ed pages of our newspapers reflect the controversy surrounding the need among many physicians to find a little time for themselves in a profession that historically has required near constant availability. Phrased somewhat negatively, they ask whether it is possible to be a "part time" physician.

The New York Times ran an Op Ed piece stating physicians need to return to the practice of expending themselves selflessly for their patients and be less concerned about their personal needs. In reply, this is how one physician feels:

I am a full-time emergency physician. I am also pregnant with my first child and planning to go part time after the delivery. Dr. Karen S. Sibert [the author of the Op Ed piece] writes that we have a "moral obligation" to serve our patients. What about our moral obligation to our children?

The sacrifices that my family and I have made should be enough. My parents spent more than $350,000 to send me to college and medical school, and I have spent nearly a decade of my life in medical school, residency and fellowship training. I have spent nights and weekends in the hospital — often missing family events, weddings and holidays in the process — and I have seen plenty of women put their personal lives on hold for their medical careers.

Dr. Sibert claims that "medicine shouldn't be a part-time interest to be set aside if it becomes inconvenient." I would argue that the same holds true for my child.

The New York Times, 06.15.2011

Today, significantly fewer physicians maintain solo practices. Doctors are forming group practices or choosing to work for large organizations or medical centers. There are three reasons: to provide better patient care, greater financial security and thirdly (and what most would say is the major reason), a more balanced lifestyle. They can have a life apart from work. As one physician told me, "Now I have a schedule...I know when I'll be working...When I'm not around I know my patients will receive good care...I can't tell you how important that is for me at this time in my life...Another perk is knowing that in a few years I'm entitled to a six month sabbatical."

Most of us are not physicians. However, we struggle with the same issue of trying to balance a desire to reach out selflessly to others in caring ways and at the same time care for ourselves. On the need to reach out selflessly, Mitch Albom, author of *Tuesdays With Morrie* learned, "The way you get meaning into your life is to devote yourself to loving others, devote yourself to your community around you, and devote yourself to creating something that gives you purpose and meaning." Yet it was Shakespeare who reminded us that we must also care for ourselves. "Self-love is not so vile a sin as self-neglect."

Is it too idealistic to nurture both our selves and others? Not at all. Walk into any nursing home, medical center, or physician practice and you will find remarkable women and men who have learned to care for themselves while serving others. If you find persons within these organizations who are discontented, unhappy, or chronically frustrated, chances are that they have lost this balance. It is not only possible to care for ourselves as we care for others, it is necessary.

Has this been your experience? ❤

Notes ⤳

Notes

Notes ~

Notes ➳

How We Learn *to* Work

"The adult ability to work is the product of a long series of individual experiences, events, and circumstances, which occur within a very complex matrix of social demands, expectations, and mores. One of our major challenges is to understand how a child becomes a working adult."

WALTER S. NEFF, MD, IN WORK AND HUMAN BEHAVIOR

A phlebotomist once told me that she thought there were two groups of employees in health care: "big people" and "little people." She counted herself among the little ones, and physicians, nurses and managers among the big ones. "After all," she explained, "without big people, patients would never be helped. People like me are easily replaceable."

How did she learn to think of herself as replaceable? Somewhere along the line, this phlebotomist must have learned that her value stemmed primarily, if not solely, from what she did, not who she was and the contributions she made as a person. As Wayne Dyer, the popular author of self-help books, famously said, "If we are what we do, then when we don't or can't, we aren't."[1a]

Those of us who share the phlebotomist's perspective could learn something from a woman who embodies the notion that our value as individuals transcends our ability to do things. Five years ago and two years into a happy second marriage, this hard-working, vibrant mother of three grown children was diagnosed with a fatal illness: Amyotrophic Lateral Sclerosis, or Lou Gehrig's disease. She functioned rather well for a couple of years before being confined to a wheelchair and then bed. With the help of hospice, her husband cared for her at home throughout the illness. She depended entirely on caregivers during the last year of her life; she couldn't move even her head or limbs. But her mind was sharp and, up until the last week or two, she could speak softly, though with difficulty.

Remarkably, this woman remained engaged in life. She wanted to live to see her daughter's child born. She also wanted to know about the interests of her other children and how her husband was coping with her illness. She was even concerned about the loss of an elderly neighbor and continued to pray for former co-workers. She wasn't afraid to continue living nor afraid to die. During the last days, caregivers asked if she wanted medication to reduce the pain. Aware that it might hasten her death, she responded, "No, not yet." She died two days later.

This was a person who knew that her value wasn't tied to what she could or couldn't do. While *doing* is one side of life, *being* is the other. Both are of inestimable value. That's something every one of us needs to discover because it fundamentally shifts how we view and operate in the world. It changes the way we love, and consequently how we live and work.

When we ponder how our work personality and attitudes toward work are formed, we start to ask questions about who shaped the way we perceive others at work, how we assess our contributions as workers, and how we relate to colleagues and authority in the workplace. How do we learn to recognize our value as persons? Who taught us? Were parents, teachers, or peers the greatest influencers? Did friends or the media play a role? How does personality affect the way we value ourselves? Why do some people overvalue work and others think it's a curse? Why is my husband a terror at home but, according to his colleagues, a great guy at work?

These are complex questions with multi-faceted answers. Let's take a closer look at how our work personalities form, keeping in mind Einstein's maxim that explanations "should be made as simple as possible, but not one bit simpler"[1] and Alfred North Whitehead's advice for those who are quick to make sweeping generalizations: "Seek simplicity, and distrust it."[2]

Case Study

I think that health care is a classroom of sorts. When providers see patients, they see themselves. It's not long before they wonder why some patients are pleasant and others so difficult? Why are two individuals who are similar in age, gender, and diagnosis have different attitudes and interact differently with people, especially their caregivers? Will I be a difficult patient if I become ill? Will caregivers think of me as someone who has aged gracefully?

Joan Chittister, an astute commentator on the human condition and herself a senior, believes that age doesn't change us:

We don't, by nature, sour as we get older. The fact is that we have always been sour, but [as we age] we take the liberty of doing it with impunity. We don't get softer as we get older. We simply get to be more unabashedly loving every day of our lovable old lives. We only get to be more of what we have always wanted to be. We are free now to choose the way we live in the world, the way we relate to the world around us, the attitudes we take into life, the meaning we get out of it, the gifts we put into it. [2a]

In some ways, we are all just getting to be more of who and what we have always been. Which means, of course, that we can decide right now what we intend to be like when we're 80: Approachable and lovable, or tyrannous and fractious.

YOUR INSIGHT: _____

_____

_____

_____

LESSON: How we decide to live today, both at home and at work, is how we will live tomorrow.

How Work Personalities Take Shape

The personalities we bring to work were molded over time in four stages. Although the biological roots of this development are guesswork, we can safely say that the first stage begins in the earliest years when we experience maternal and paternal loves. In the second stage, we learn about work during the early school years. The third stage involves learning our family's attitudes toward work. In the fourth stage, at least initially, we begin to identify with like-minded individuals in jobs, professions, trades, careers, or callings.

Some researchers think personalities are a semi-autonomous part of us. This explains a common phenomenon—the sense that an individual is one person at home and another at work. While our work personalities are largely formed by the time we reach our thirties, researchers agree that the way we work will likely change as we continue to learn throughout adult life.[3]

Looking back on the four stages is one way to see what needs to change as we move into a more desirable future.

Stage One: Maternal *and* Paternal Loves

It may seem like a stretch, but our work personalities actually begin to be shaped in infancy. Before you reject this idea, imagine it's early morning, before sunrise and the rush of day has begun. A mother sits holding her just-awakened baby daughter, a tender moment for both. As baby stirs, the mother scans her as only a mother can. She looks at the bright eyes, notices the smooth, almost transparent skin, and then runs her fingers though the wispy hair as she feeds her baby. When their eyes meet, the baby squirms. The mother smiles and the two are enmeshed in a moment of pure togetherness. To an observer, this interaction, while difficult to measure, suggests something special is going on between mother and infant. It is maternal love, an observable affection that the mother freely gives.

Now imagine the setting a few minutes later. The baby has stopped feeding and starts to fidget, then screws up her face and lets out a whimper. Every mother knows what that means: a bowel movement. She raises baby from her lap, catches a whiff to confirm what she suspects, and gives baby a big hug. "Good girl," she whispers. "Good poop." That moment is no less intimate than the first. It is an instance of paternal love—an earned affection.

Fast-forward a few years. Now picture the baby as a young adult having had many maternal and paternal love experiences. Through maternal love, she will have known what it feels like to be loved for no other reason than she is lovable. Through paternal love, she will have known what it feels like to be loved for doing a good job.

Unlike this child, some people grow up without having received a balance of maternal and paternal loves. Maybe they got too much paternal love and not enough maternal love. You would know this by observing their behavior. They make their beds, are quiet at the appropriate times, study hard, treat their little sisters well, and always try to please their parents. These youngsters are experts at knowing how to gain a paternal type of love. But they'll likely grow up feeling an emptiness inside that no amount of paternal love can satisfy. That emptiness is an absence of maternal love. They've become competent, responsible, dutiful, hard-working adults and may even excel at what they do. But they also feel an inner restlessness. No amount of affirmation will ever fill the bottomless, insatiable void.

What about kids who experience an abundance of maternal love but a dearth of "earned" paternal love, which is equally important? Their parents may have said, "You failed algebra? That's OK. We love you." "Other kids are picking on you? Shame on them. We love you." Although such unconditional love is essential, if it's not balanced by paternal love that rewards effort, the child fears doing and achieving. Having never learned the give and take of the competitive world with its frustrations and rewards, she becomes an adult who feels uncomfortable among doers. She may recoil from a challenge because she hasn't learned how to overcome failure or been encouraged to pick herself up and try again.

As you can see, parenting styles have a big impact on our workplace personalities. Growing up, those who earned paternal love but not enough maternal love will yearn for something that no amount of work can satisfy. Those who didn't earn sufficient paternal love will find themselves uneasy in, and ill-equipped for, the workaday world, with its deadlines, competition, and successes as well as failures.

A real-life example is Janet. Forty-five years old, happily married, the mother of three, Janet is grateful to be a doctor and relishes helping others, particularly the disadvantaged. When she chose to become a primary care physician, she knew that gastroenterologists and vascular surgeons earned higher salaries. Yet she felt that working as a primary care physician would be more rewarding in the long run.

Over the years, Janet has become comfortable with that career decision. She appreciates patients' kind words and her good reputation in her community. As busy as she is, she has not lost sight of the people who supported her, particularly her husband and her physician-mentor, now a dear friend. Both affirmed Janet's desire to become a family physician at a time when she questioned her ability to complete her training.

Some of her colleagues don't like being on call, but Janet doesn't mind. She says she actually likes it when someone needs her unexpectedly. Precisely because she chose primary care rather than a specialty, Janet has time to be home with her kids almost every night, unlike many peers. She keeps her practice small. Janet's business partner and fellow physician, Megan, covers for her when she needs to be out of the office for several days.

Janet's parents, while certainly loving, had high expectations of her as a child. Good grades were non-negotiable and rewarded accordingly. Graduate school was expected yet seldom mentioned. Her parents were somewhat demanding, but often they affirmed her efforts. She never doubted their pride in her. Janet has always liked working, even when she worked as a waitress to get through college. "I'm pretty confident I can learn to do just about any job as long as I put my mind to it," she says.

She met Megan during residency training. Despite their different personalities, they hit it off immediately. Both knew the other was smart. Each liked to have a good time. And they shared the same professional goal: To work in a small family practice and thereby avoid the politics of a large, multi-physician group. But their home lives while growing up were quite a contrast.

Janet remembers how her parents affirmed her success in school and sports. Her father even tutored her in chemistry during junior year in high school. "He made chemistry interesting," she says. "I think he thought I wouldn't like the sciences because I was a girl. Wrong! While my parents were relatively directive and forceful, I never got the feeling that I wasn't loved. In fact, I felt just the opposite."

Megan's parents divorced after she left for college. "I saw it coming," she recalls. "It was a good thing. I'm still close to both, but closer to my mother. I could see that they had grown apart. Neither of them was very expressive. My father was better at showing affection than my mother. While both of them would tell me they loved me, and I believed them, I never really felt it. They definitely were pleased with my marks in school and the fact that I got an academic scholarship to college, but their repeated expression of 'good job' never seemed enough. To this day, believe it or not, as worthwhile as it is being a physician, I still feel a little empty. Janet tells me she can't understand why I feel as I do."

Janet says of Megan: "She's a jewel, generous to a fault. She even overextends herself, for which I'm personally appreciative. However, I know that her generosity is not going to take away her feelings of emptiness and not being enough. I wish it were otherwise. Even though I let her know that I'm grateful for everything she does—she's super competent and detail oriented—she never seems to feel my support. The way I see it, she works like a Trojan, but all of her dedication is not getting her what she needs and expects from work."

These descriptions reveal the impact that maternal and paternal loves have had on Janet's and Megan's lives to this day. Janet apparently experienced both types. She is pleased with herself and enjoys her work. Megan, in contrast, apparently experienced much paternal love—her accomplishments earned recognition, for example—but little maternal love. Thus her feelings of never being "enough." She is restless and no amount of doing will get her what she unknowingly craves—love bestowed only because she is lovable.

These two physicians could be any of us. We've all worked with colleagues who, although highly respected and affirmed, feel restless and consistently underappreciated. Maybe we ourselves have felt that way at times. Conversely, we all know someone who grew up with an abundance of maternal love but pulls back when an opportunity will entail competition, deadlines, or expectations.

On page 68, you'll learn about the impact that schooling has on work behaviors.

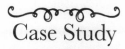

Case Study

An accomplished professional woman who, "recovering" from work addiction, has spent years in therapy and meditative, journal-writing practice:

"I was always told I was 'smart' and so I figured I should be able to catch on to any subject without working at it. If I didn't understand or, better yet, master the subject or activity immediately, I berated myself as not being smart. That led to feelings of being an impostor. I assumed I should automatically be able to speak Greek, play piano, or learn anything the first time it was introduced. I thought practice was for sissies.

"Then the self-berating for not being smart pre-empted any possible learning. As a professional, this attitude expressed itself as the self-sabotaging behavior of not preparing for a presentation. I told myself that I should be able to 'wing it' and that professionals don't need to rehearse or prepare for presentations, no matter how large the audience.

"After many public humiliations in which I sweated through presentations, almost fainted once, and mostly did OK but occasionally fell short, I began to experience an almost paralyzing fear of speaking. This was definitely career-limiting. I realized that my attitude of thinking that I was somehow 'too good to prepare' was self-defeating. I had an epiphany and understood on a much deeper level that the need to study or practice was nothing to be ashamed about and that, in fact, I was actually giving myself a gift by preparing. With my next presentation, I started to do just that, preparing three months in advance just to see if I would experience speaking differently. It was a miracle! Imagine that! When you prepare, you feel competent, comfortable, and can even have fun.

"So, it's a relief to know that everyone needs to practice something to be good at it. I know this sounds pathetically self-evident and basic, but that was my path. I'm sure my parents thought they were doing the right thing for my self-esteem by telling me I was smart, etc., but I took it to mean that I should automatically know everything and, if I didn't, I wasn't smart.

"Now, as a parent, I've fallen into the same trap as my parents, thinking I'm doing my 12-year-old son a favor by telling him how smart and talented he is rather than emphasizing the importance of practice, learning, and effort. He's even told me that when I brag about him, it puts too much pressure on him to do something well. Funny how we teach what we have to learn and how, if we don't learn it the first time around, there are many other ways to learn it again!

YOUR INSIGHT:

_____

_____

_____

_____

LESSON: Reflection and self awareness are the beginning of changing self-defeating behaviors. None of us are "too good" to prepare and work at becoming competent.

Taking Notes
Your Gift to Yourself

On this journey to gain insight into why we work the way we do, it's helpful to jot down your thoughts along the way. This book provides journaling space after each Tip, at the end of each chapter and at the end of the book for you to record your personal reflections. You can keep this book private, not showing it to anyone—not even a spouse, best friend, lover, or counselor. At some future point, you may choose to share your writing with them so they have a window into your internal life. But for now, consider this book your private space to express your innermost thoughts and feelings without fear of criticism. It's also a place to be honest about what you're thinking and feeling at that moment, recognizing that your thoughts and feelings may be different at another time.

Note to Self: You'll get the most out of your notes, both in the moment and later on, if you create the opportunity to write flowingly, without an internal editor or judge. Let your musings roam beyond only a sentence or two if you can. The more you write, the more you'll benefit from your reflective time. Very likely, and perhaps surprisingly, you'll find it makes you feel good to get these inner thoughts down on paper. Try to take your time and write until you feel you're finished for now. There's no telling how long that might be; it varies from one person to the next, which is why there are additional pages in the back for those moments when the ideas flow.

You are encouraged to wait until your journal thoughts have dwindled and there's nothing more to write before you continue reading. This may be in an hour, in a day, or longer. Enjoy this reflective process as a gift you're giving to yourself.

Based on the information you just read about maternal and paternal love, jot down the first thoughts that come to mind when you read the following questions:

- Do I have particularly memorable experiences of *maternal* love?

- Do I have particularly memorable experiences of *paternal* love?

- Looking back over the years, what do I remember about the way my parents showed me their love?

By writing down your thoughts about your childhood experiences, you gain a greater understanding of where your responses and reactions to bosses, authority figures and coworkers may have originated. See if you're recreating your childhood at work. This can be the start of improving your relationships at work.

Case Study

CLEARING OUT THE MENTAL CLUTTER

"The Materials Management Department suggested that we have an 'amnesty day' during which every department would go through desks, cabinets, and store rooms to find and discard what was no longer being used. Thinking that the amount of trash could be substantial, they leased a dumpster and placed it in the employee parking lot.

"The nursing managers and facilities people thought it was a particularly good idea and got behind it.

"What went into the dumpsters? Stacks and stacks of unused and outdated forms, boxes of undistributed newsletters, obsolete policy manuals, stained chairs, broken tables, typewriters, and cartons of dated supplies that managers considered valueless. The exercise began on Monday. On Tuesday, they leased three more dumpsters.

"What started as a playful housecleaning initiative turned into a serious competitive sport. We challenged each other to see who could throw out the most junk. By Wednesday evening, five dumpsters had been filled.

"This week, during a change-in-shift meeting, one of the evening nurses who was not part of the venture noted that she now found it easier to work. 'I know where things are, it's not all cluttered up, I even know what we don't have and need to order,' she said.

"A case manager at the meeting said that the project prompted her to think about herself: 'All week I've been wondering if the clutter in my head keeps me from living well.' She is young in years yet wise of mind and heart."

YOUR INSIGHT:

_____

_____

_____

_____

LESSON: If we are to work well together, don't we all need an 'amnesty day' to clear the clutter of hurts, regrets, failures, betrayals, and resentments stored inside of us?

Stage Two: Schooling

Along with our experiences of maternal and paternal love, early schooling is also a significant factor influencing our workplace personalities. Challenges we face in adjusting to the classroom mirror those that we encounter on the job years later. How we adjust to the former is a harbinger of the latter.

The moment formal schooling begins, whether in a traditional or less-structured setting, children:

- Will have tasks to perform. Their "job" may include learning how to read, memorizing the multiplication table, and keeping a tidy desk;

- Must complete tasks among peers, apart from their families;

- Must function under an authority apart from their parents;

- Must adjust to the clock and learn to distinguish between designated times for work or play;

- Will feel success as well as failure; and

- Will see individuals being unequally rewarded (and experience unfair treatment themselves).

Similarly, the workplace requires that we follow bosses' direction, work cooperatively, balance work and free time, handle the highs and lows of success and failure, and adjust to disappointing or even unjust situations. How we react and adapt to salaries, bonuses, promotions, titles, days off, or even the assignment of office space harken back to the adjustments we made at school.

Few researchers would suggest a cause-and-effect relationship between any particular schooling experience and the formation of work personality. But they do know that early schooling is formative.[4]

Post-secondary education also has an immense and lasting impact on work personality. Surely college changed the way you think, what you value, and how you live and work. Self-learning and life experiences affect us, too. So how can we say that our personalities are formed early in life, then turn around and claim that what we learn in college or on the job changes us in profound ways?

To understand this seeming contradiction, imagine a co-worker who has been placed on a corrective action plan. He seldom completes his assignments on time and frets over details to such an extent that he sometimes doesn't finish projects. He's a likeable chap with good intentions, but a terrible performer.

The corrective action plan requires that he see a counselor. Being a good-hearted fellow who wants to keep his job and improve his performance, he complies. After a session or two, the counselor suspects that the client's difficulties stem at least in part from his obsessive-compulsive ways. His personality is somewhat set and not likely to change, so the counselor teaches the troubled employee how to develop new habits that will help him adjust to work. However, those learned behaviors won't change the obsessive-compulsive tendencies that took root when he was a boy. What will have changed is his ability to recognize such tendencies and not give in to them. Consequently, he will work in less self-defeating ways.

For years, clinicians used various types of therapy to try to reconstruct the underlying structure of patients' personalities. That effort has largely been abandoned. In its place are medical and cognitive therapies that help people leverage their strengths and adjust to their shortcomings.

Families of origin also shape the way we work, as you'll see on page 72.

Tip No. 1
to Help Ourselves

Recall what you learned *about* work *from* your school years

In the blank writing pages at the end of this chapter, reflect on the six structures common to schooling and the workplace (page 68). Let your mind roam—write what immediately comes to you, unfiltered by any judgment or analysis. You may be surprised by how much you remember. Allow the flow of writing and seemingly random thoughts continue in a welcome jumble of ideas and memories.

Once you've emptied your thoughts on paper, turn to these questions to awaken additional memories:

- As a child, was it easy for you to adjust to the clock?

- Is it easy or difficult for you to work on a schedule today?

- How did you respond as a child when you saw your classmates treated unfairly by peers or teachers?

- Do you recall specific instances of being treated fairly or unfairly? Describe them and how you felt at the time using as much detail as you can.

- Did you look forward to going to school? Did you dread the beginning of, and returning to school each year?

- Did you feel like an outsider there?

- What did you learn about authority figures—the principal and your teachers—at school?

- When you were a child, was there someone you wanted to become? Who? Did that change over the years?

Extra Credit for Extra Insight!

- As you matured into a young adult, who did you want to become?

- Did school help you become aware of the type of work you would enjoy?

- How did school positively and negatively prepare you for the workplace?

- Do you have a dream that has lived in your heart over the years? Have you followed it? Has it been dampened? Are you following the dream now?

Spend some time thinking about and responding to these questions. Hopefully, they'll spur additional, deeper thoughts.

THE BENEFIT TO YOU: The questions you answer in Tip No. 1 may yield new insights that will be useful in exploring how and why you work and view your career as you do. ❧

Stage Three: Learning *within* Families *of* Origin

Families of origin are immensely important in shaping the way we work. Their influence is especially significant because family life extends for years across several stages of development. Formal conversations and everyday banter are one influence; how family members work together and resolve conflicts are another.[5]

What child has not heard, "Sticks and stones may break my bones, but names will never hurt me"? The fact is, words do matter. They can destroy as well as heal and they have a lasting, sometimes lifelong, impact.

We live in "verbal universes" that are as real as the table on which I write or the chair on which you sit. For example, suppose a child overhears his father speaking with the boy's older brother. "You don't need to go to college," he says. "I didn't. It would be better for you to get a job." Such words can linger in the boy's and his brother's memories for years. As an adult, the younger brother may or may not follow the advice given to his older brother, yet the father's attitude will influence his attitudes and choices.

Researchers have long noted how children tend to disproportionately choose their parents' interests and careers. The parents of classical pianists often are or were musicians, and higher-than-expected percentages of nurses come from families in which one or the other parent is or was a nurse. Preachers' children are likely to become preachers. An unusually high percentage of Nobel Laureates are sons and daughters of scientists. Clearly, while many factors affect a child's choice of profession, the verbal universe at home is a formidable influence.

Equally influential on work attitudes are the relational dynamics within families.[6] At work, you may have heard others say, "We're a family around here," meaning employees genuinely care for each other. They feel connected, supportive, and committed to one another. If, in our childhood home, we cultivated a habit of thinking positively of others, as adults we'll think that way at work, too. If our family encouraged direct communication among its members, we'll communicate directly with others on the job. Conversely, if our family taught us to blame others when things went wrong, we'll probably blame others at work. And on it goes. Family dynamics are learned patterns of behavior that become deeply embedded in our personalities and stay with us when we grow up and leave home.

Over time, most people appreciate the values that were instilled in them as children and acknowledge that those values serve them well at work. However, some behavior patterns learned in childhood don't serve us well in adulthood. If we grew up in a family dominated by an alcoholic parent, an abusive uncle, or a seriously depressed sibling, we had to develop coping strategies to survive. One highly sophisticated strategy is to minimize or even deny the seriousness of a family problem. But minimizing problems as defenseless children growing up in a terrifying, out-of-control situation won't help us survive later on in a dysfunctional workplace.

A couple's marital difficulties illustrate some of the more subtle ways that we carry childhood lessons into the workplace. Suppose this couple discovers that their teenage daughter has a drug problem. Family therapists wouldn't be surprised to learn that the parents focus all of their attention on trying to fix her problem and ignore the impact that their troubled relationship likely has on the daughter's ability to cope with stresses in her life. When parents have conflicts, and stress and arguments are steady undercurrents in a tense household, children's daily ups and downs, struggles at school, and angst about peer relationships get lost. Parents focus on the "problem child" rather than deal directly with their relationship and its contribution to family turmoil. In the language of therapists, they triangulate—

that is, focus on a third person to avoid confronting their own problems.

Have you seen examples of this dynamic in the workplace? It might look like this: Two colleagues who don't get along with each other—think "parents," as in the earlier example—talk about a manager's faults instead of their own conflict. They may not even be aware they're triangulating.

Another negative dynamic learned at home is scapegoating—blaming someone else for something that has gone wrong rather than taking responsibility for one's own role in the incident. The target is usually a person who's absent or perceived as weaker. At work, a scapegoater might say, "It's his fault, not mine." In childhood, she may have successfully avoided responsibility by, for example, blaming her younger brother for breaking Mother's favorite vase.

The CEO of a highly regarded medical center in the Midwest recruited Olga as chief nursing officer to overcome lingering conflict among the directors of four units in the nursing department. After less than a month on the job, Olga said she felt like she was managing children instead of working with adults. One of the directors thought Olga was naïve and, when an issue arose, would speak only to the hospital administrator, who, in her opinion, was more realistic and better understood the challenges she faced. Two other directors were dutiful; they consistently checked with the new CNO before making decisions. "They wanted to please me so much it was starting to drive me crazy," Olga said.

The fourth nursing director was somewhat of a mystery. She came to meetings, seldom spoke, and was always pleasant. After three months, in a report the CEO had asked Olga to submit, including assessments of the four directors, Olga wrote this about the quiet one: "She seems to survive by keeping her head down."

This true story illustrates how words and dynamics learned at home transfer to the workplace. I don't agree with Olga's perception that she was working with children. Rather, the nursing directors had learned effective behaviors in their childhood families and, as adults, incorporated these behaviors into their managerial style and relationships with co-workers.

I was a consultant to this medical center's senior team. Years earlier, when I had a large psychotherapy practice, a client of mine was a nurse manager on the senior team—the same person who later became a unit director who constantly tried to please Olga. In childhood, this nurse was obsessed with pleasing her mother and afraid to displease her father, a high-profile lawyer. At age 49, she still called her mother three or four times a week. No wonder she also needed to please Olga and nearly drove her crazy by checking in so often.

As for the nurse who kept her head down, she and I had served on another hospital's senior team. One of five children who grew up in an abusive home, where two brothers were beaten "for no other reason than my mother was under stress," she recalled an incident in which the brothers were squabbling about something: "My mother jumped up and hit my oldest brother. It was chaotic. I survived by being quiet and responsible. I did well in school but that was to avoid my mother's wrath as much as it was that I liked my teachers." This woman had advanced as a nurse manager by being quiet. People liked her. She never took sides. I'm not aware of a time she ever rocked the boat.

Although I don't know anything about the other nurse managers' family lives, I suspect that they, too, brought coping strategies from their childhood years to the workplace. All of us do.

After you've completed the following exercise, turn to page 81 to learn about the fourth stage of developing a work personality.

ॐ

Tip No. 2

to Help Ourselves

ॐ

Reflect *on* how your family *has* shaped *the* way you work

Ponder each of the following questions for a time, even a day or two, before jotting down some of your thoughts. Allowing your thoughts to quietly simmer for a few days will awaken memories and likely yield insights. When you're ready, consider these questions and take notes on what comes to mind:

- Did your parent(s) speak with you explicitly about the job or profession they expected you to pursue?

- What do you think were your parents' unspoken hopes regarding your job, career, or profession? What hopes did they express?

- Looking back, would you have wanted your parent(s) to give you more or less direction as your life unfolded? Why?

- What role did family members play in how you learned to work?

- When you looked for work, did family members support your efforts? Or did you feel like you were competing with them? Did you ever get the sense they hoped that your search would fail?

Extra Credit for Extra Insight!

- How did your family teach you to handle conflict?

- How did your family teach you to handle failure?

- How did your family teach you to handle success?

- What did your family teach you about employment and earning a salary or how much you should earn?

- Have you worked in a place where there is a family spirit? If so, what's appealing about such a place? What is limiting? Do work relationships remind you of your childhood family dynamics at home? If so, what was your role in the family? What's your role at work?

THE BENEFIT TO YOU: Giving yourself the gift of this reflective time will reap great rewards. Seeing the underlying patterns of how our work relationships were formed is the first step to changing our interactions and approach to work. ℰ

Case Study

JOB CHOICE AND FAMILY DYNAMICS

This nurse describes how her upbringing led to her decision to become a nurse and how it influences the way she cares for patients.

"I was the fifth of seven children, raised on a farm outside of Urbana, Illinois. By the time me and my brother came along, my parents were tired of being parents; my sisters and brothers talk about how strict my parents were, but the rules relaxed for me and my brother. You might say we were the victims of benign neglect.

My mother was a remarkable woman. She also grew up on a farm and after graduating high school she stayed back to help her mother. The next year, my mother and father married and by age 31, she had seven children and they owned the farm.

My mother's philosophy of life can be summarized in a few well-worn phrases. Be faithful, honest, and cooperate with one another. Share your time, energy and money. Be patient and forgiving. Don't be selfish. Count your blessings especially your health. Don't complain. Be polite. Her values were reflected in other sayings such as do your best, be ambitious but don't step on others. Attend to your appearance. Be glamorous but not ostentatious. Don't quit. Control you temper. Never be vulgar.

My mother was the glue that kept the family together. I remember how she nudged us kids to get an education. While she didn't go to college, every one of us did, three with scholarships to the University of Illinois. During my early teens my father started to drink. He wasn't drunk all the time but he would drink at the end of a long day in the fields. My mother didn't like it and showed her disapproval by silence and a kind of coldness. She was full of anger toward him.

By the time I was seventeen he was a full-fledged drunk. He could still do some farm work in the morning but by evening he was out of it. The man who could be so playful when I was a youngster became a bitter not-so-old grouch when drunk. The change was remarkable. At night he needed help to get into bed. I was the one who did that. I think my mother was simply disgusted and furious. I didn't share her coldness toward him.

I was naive about alcoholism; my mom and us kids were really enablers. When I finally sought help, the counselor called me codependent. That label is true but it misses the fact that caring for my father awakened within me a genuine empathy for those who are ill. It's not surprising that I received an RN followed by a BA. You don't have to be a shrink to see the connection between my family life and choice of profession.

My father died at a relatively young age from his addiction. If there is a silver lining to my story, it is that patients often tell me there is something special about me and they want me as their nurse. That makes me think of my father. Because of him, I know what it means to be present and caring and to expect nothing in return. That attitude is in the heart of every nurse who is truly a nurse.

I'm actually grateful I had an alcoholic father. I know the dark side of alcoholism and what it does to the family, but through it I was led into a profession that I relish. I was surprised to learn that children of alcoholics represent a larger than expected percentage of individuals who choose the nursing profession. It is a short step to see the connection.

I believe life not only influences your choice of work, but how you work. I've had to learn new ways to deal with anger, avoid denial, and be honest and direct in my communication with others. This inner work has led to self awareness, which has allowed me to be ever more present with my patients."

YOUR INSIGHT: _____

_____

_____

_____

_____

LESSON: Examine how your early childhood is influencing your career choice and how you work.

Stage Four: Forming *a* Work Identity

In this fourth and final stage, we come to identify with others who have similar talents that lead to similar employment. When strangers meet for the first time, one often asks the other, "What do you do?" The person who has successfully developed a work identity answers, "I'm a salesman," "case manager," "policeman," "phlebotomist." There's no hesitation or awkwardness—"This is who I am and who I like to be." They both identify with that title and have a common, underlying bond based on work identity.

I knew a young woman who said she always wanted to be a nurse. After graduating from high school, she earned an associate degree in licensed practical nursing. On the job, she thought of herself as a nurse but felt uncomfortable around seasoned nurses. She once told me, "I don't really feel that I am a nurse when I'm with them."

The hospital where she worked subsidized the cost of ongoing education, so she decided to return to school for a bachelor of arts degree. Teachers encouraged this gifted student to continue on for a master's degree. Last year, after graduating with a master's, she told the chief nursing officer, "I finally feel like I'm a nurse." She had developed a work identity. As the years pass, she may develop others, but the first one is immensely important. She belongs to a group and will enjoy respite from the youthful task of becoming "someone." When she meets an unfamiliar physician in the cafeteria who greets her with, "Hi! I'm Dr. Martinez. I don't think we've met," she'll quickly and proudly respond, "Nice to meet you. I'm Jessica. I'm a nurse on the OB unit."

Most people develop a work identity by their late twenties or early thirties. Largely through hard work and sometimes by sheer good fortune, we become politicians, researchers, stay-at-home parents, pastors, insurance executives, or nurses. The identity gives us a sense of community and belonging.

However, not everyone is so fortunate, as this first-person story illustrates:

"I got out of college two years ago. I've always wanted to become an actor, so I moved to Los Angeles. I didn't know a soul. I bounced in and out of a couple of small parts in a couple of productions, but I wasn't making it. I supported myself by walking peoples' dogs and waiting tables. Man, it was boring. It's difficult for me to say I'm an actor when I don't get paid for acting. Now I'm not so sure acting is what I want. My friend says I'd make a good massage therapist. That's what she is. Maybe she's right. In any case, she's moving back to Maine and I'm going with her. I heard that there is a need for fishermen and artists in Camden, Maine. We'll see."

Although this not-so-young man doesn't seem particularly anxious about landing a job and finding a work identity, his words are a little misleading. He's very concerned and actually feels badly about himself. The challenge he faces, as all of us do, is to find employment that fits his inner self. Until that occurs, an academic degree, a trade, or a developed skill is only a step in the right direction.

If someone gets a job that doesn't seem to tap his talents or fit his self-image, he may still be a good employee, especially if he's hardworking and conscientious. But he must also live with the frustration that ultimately comes with this choice. Such frustration makes some people feel, mistakenly, like an imposter or fraud. The fact is, they simply work in a job or have responsibilities that are dissonant with their competencies and talents.

This fourth stage in the development of work personalities is particularly important because it links us to a community of mostly like-minded individuals, even if we work alone. For instance, it's well- documented that people who identify themselves as writers feel a bond with other writers, be they nearby or far away. Identity transcends physical proximity. It's a sense of shared values and perspective, and of similar personality styles and preferences. The groups we identify with influence how we think and what we value. Dockworkers, lawyers, teachers, nurses—all are members of professional groups that not only share many of the same abilities, but have many of the same values, talents, and traits in common. Once you become a dockworker, you'll soon think and vote like your fellow dockworkers.

While finding a work identity as a young adult is necessary, the identity probably won't last forever. A man who once thought of himself as a teacher may leave that profession and enter politics. Chemists morph into teachers and physicians become pastors. However, the first work identity gives us confidence and a footing to make further choices. Without that initial identity, developing a new one is difficult. For the man described earlier who toyed with acting as a career, becoming a fisherman or artist would be considerably easier if he had the confidence arising from having succeeded as an actor. Success and achievement breed future accomplishment.

For some people, work identity evolves into a calling rather than a specific type of work. An example is a friend of mine who is leaving one job in search of another. Some call her foolish. I think she's alive, talented, and high-functioning—a real a catch for anyone who employs her. Here's her story:

After college, this woman left her homeland and traveled to the United States "just because I was young and it was exciting to think of living in a foreign country." She couldn't find a job immediately, so she went to graduate school for a year, earned a business degree, and immediately landed a job with a consulting company. She loved it. Five years later, she noticed that the local university had a teaching position open. They were looking for "a creative, inspiring, generalist who could teach incoming freshmen the value of a liberal arts education." She said to herself, "That's me!" So she applied and got the job. She did that successfully for another six years.

At age 32, the same feelings that had stirred her during college surfaced again. "Even though I was happy at the university, I felt that I needed to jump ship and enter the seminary," she says. "Everyone thought I was loony, but I did it anyway." Four years later, she graduated from a premier school on the East Coast with a master's degree in divinity and soon became pastor of a little Presbyterian church in New England. For the first time in her life, she thought of her work as a calling. She was often heard to say that as a pastor, she learned the difference between having a vocation and having a job.

Those thoughts and feelings were relatively short-lived, however. On her 41st birthday, four years into her ministry, she admitted that she had become increasingly depressed. The church elders knew something wasn't right and counseled her to look for another type of ministry. "The role does not fit you," they told her, "You care about people, but you get overwhelmed by their needs."

What happened? "Going down that path to become a pastor almost nine years ago was the best thing that ever happened to me," she told me. "Back then, I equated being 'called' with doing church work. Now, when I look back, I see a pattern that has run through my entire life. My calling isn't this or that job. What all those jobs have in common is my desire to care for people. That's my vocation, whether I'm a consultant, teacher, or pastor."

Like her, maybe more of us should start thinking about patterns in our life histories. This would bring greater insight and self awareness so we can make conscious career choices that best fit who we are. Being in the right job brings meaning and satisfaction to our work and to our lives beyond work.

By the end of the second or third decade of life, we will have traversed all four stages in the development of our workplace personality. As mentioned earlier, some researchers see this personality as a semi-autonomous part of us[7] which is why we may be serious, unemotional, and meticulous at work, and then, in the safe haven of home, we loosen up, lighten our mood, and may even be a little messy in the kitchen.

It's important to remember that work personality is malleable, something that John O'Donohue, a poet, philosopher, and scholar, understands well when he writes: *"Though the human body is born complete in one moment, the birth of the human heart is an ongoing process. It is being birthed in every experience of your life. Everything that happens to you has the potential to deepen you. It brings to birth within you new territories of the heart."*[8]

Tip No. 3 — Understanding your work identity: What type *of* people *do* you genuinely identify with?

to Help Ourselves

Here are some questions to help you explore your work identity. Write down your thoughts as you consider the following:

- What words do I use to introduce and identify myself when I meet someone for the first time?

- How do I feel when I tell others I'm a (nurse, physician, social worker, driver, etc.)?

- In what ways am I different at home than at work?

- Am I myself at work?

- Am I myself at home?

- List the work identities you've had over the years. Do not be surprised if there are more than three:

1. _____

2. _____

3. _____

- Individuals with a well-established work identity are usually perceived as having personal authority. Do people at work take me seriously?

- Looking at this linegraph, if "I feel that I have authority when at work" is a 5 and "I feel as if I am overlooked when at work" is a 0, where do I place myself on a scale of 0 to 5?

I FEEL OVERLOOKED AT WORK   0   1   2   3   4   5   I FEEL I HAVE AUTHORITY AT WORK

THE BENEFIT TO YOU: Jotting down your thoughts here will help you answer the questions, "Who am I?" in a work context—and "How was my work identity formed and how has it changed?" What freedom it is to know ourselves better! ❧

Observe your differentness

Tip No. 4

to Help Ourselves

So far, you have reflected on your experiences in the four-stage development of work personality; clarified, at least to a degree, some of the influential forces that have shaped the way you work today; and asked yourself if there's still an ache in your heart—something you long for that no amount of work seems to satisfy. If you've felt that ache, you have also considered the possibility that your approach to work may be an effort to relieve it.

Before turning to the next chapter, jot down as clearly as you can the group or profession with whom you identify. If it's difficult to get started, pretend you meet a somewhat obnoxious person at a party who says, "Hi, I'm Jack and a friend of Jane. We work together. We're both lawyers. What do you do?" Don't be turned off by his intrusiveness. Answer him honestly.

- Is there a match between who you feel you are and what you do?

- Write about people with whom you share a work identity. In what ways are you different from them? Are you comfortable with those differences?

THE BENEFIT TO YOU: When you feel comfortable with others in your profession, you're probably in the right line of work. If you don't have much in common with others in your field perhaps it's time to rethink your career choice, or it's simply good information to consider when you're at work.

Case Study

Reflection of a clinical psychologist:

Some time ago, the news was filled with stories about the extramarital affairs of Tiger Woods. Aside from the cynics who report on celebrity figures with a what-else-is-new attitude, many people were shocked: "I always thought of him as balanced and mature, the kind of athlete we needed to help youngsters, including my children, become responsible adults. I can't stand the fact that he led two lives."

Perhaps you read about the woman who was so angry with Tiger that she wanted to go right up to him and yell, "Who are you? Damn it, tell me. Who are you really?" You could feel her letdown and disillusionment as she spoke.

I've begun to ask myself the same question. The question comes to mind because I know that I have not always lived up to others' expectations. Are there people who want to yell at me? There are surely employees who feel disappointed with my leadership. At times I have disappointed myself, particularly with things I haven't done.

Maybe there's a Tiger Woods in us all. If so, we need not throw stones at him or at ourselves. We simply need to be honest with ourselves.

In the years ahead, Mr. Woods's character will be shaped by how he faces himself. Will he continue in his old ways or will he mature as a person? The same can be said of any of us. As Helen Keller wrote, "Character cannot be developed in ease and quiet. Only through experience of trial and suffering can the soul be strengthened, ambition inspired, and success achieved."

Do you think our character as health care professionals matters? After all, patients place great trust in us. Our differing professions are esteemed. We all know that nurses are among the most trusted and valued individuals in our society. Is the character of a nurse tending to a patient, a physician making rounds, the pharmacist preparing medications, the accountant reviewing a spread sheet, the plumber monitoring the heating, ventilation, and air conditioning system, or the character of an administrator considering length-of-stay statistics an important factor in the way they carry out their duties? It was Albert Einstein who commented, "Most people say that it is the intellect which makes a great scientist. They are wrong: It is character."

YOUR INSIGHT:

LESSON: There is a Tiger in us all. Character shapes the way we care for others.

A Reflection

Within health care, some employees have highly respected titles such as "doctor" or "CEO. " Others think of themselves as managers or directors. Some proudly identify with their professions as nurses, IT techs, financial analysts, or phlebotomists. We think of ourselves as ordinary folk with important yet commonplace jobs. Theoreticians tell us that these ways of referring to ourselves reflect that we have a "work identity" which influences how we relate to one another and how we think about ourselves.

Alan Arkin, the Oscar-winning actor appeared in over eighty films. His memoir, *An Improvised Life* describes that by age five he knew he had the talent to mimic and pretend he was other people. Others recognized his extraordinary talent. No wonder he became an actor. However, over the years he began to recognize that, "...I had become an actor so as to hide, to find my identity through pretending to be other people." Despite his fame, he realized he didn't know himself. The memoir documents his journey to become himself.

The journey, he writes, changed his life. Today he remains an actor but works differently precisely because he understands who he is behind his identity as an actor. "You cannot imagine how that has changed my life, what I do and do not do, say and do not say. I wish I had known this as a young man! The problem is no one tells us. We have to learn it."

We are not in the movie business yet I suspect that we know something about which Mr. Arkin writes. We have likely developed identities similar to how Mr. Arkin developed his.

I mention this because of a phone call I just had with a youngish, wonderfully pleasant and competent employee. Her husband recently died and her only child just moved out of her home to start his life in the world as a young adult. How did she feel? "All of a sudden I was alone. I had been a mom and a caregiver of my chronically ill husband for years and years. I also really enjoyed my work within the Human Resource Department. Now I wake up and ask myself, who am I? I feel like I've forgotten to ask myself that question in the midst of working so hard and being so busy."

Mr. Arkin and this employee seem on similar journeys. Perhaps all of us are. If this is one of those times when you question your value, remember that there are times in nearly everyone's life when a comfortable identity or role is either lost or outgrown. There is something sacred, if anxious, about the moment. By facing the loss and the question of who we are apart from our roles in life, we will return to whatever we do with a personal presence, warmth and compassion that is both welcome and unmistakable. ❤

Notes ⇀

Notes ⌐⸲

Notes

Notes ⤳

Unhealthy Ways *of* Working

"The 'crazy busy' existence that so
many of us complain about is almost
entirely self-imposed."

TIM KREIDER, THE BUSY TRAP,

THE NEW YORK TIMES, 2012

Freud noted that the mark of healthy individuals is the ability to love and work; one without the other is an illness.[1a] Just as early life experiences shape our beliefs and values, and thus how we see our role in a love relationship, they shape our beliefs and values related to how we work.

Some of those experiences can distort the way we work, leading to an unbalanced, unhealthy situation in which distorted approaches—what I call work fixation, work addiction, and work exhaustion—are praised and rewarded. Let's take a closer look at the symptoms of these distorted, unhealthy ways to work, the purposes they serve, and the problems they can cause for us and our families, loved ones, and co-workers.

Work Fixation

Work-fixated individuals approach every activity in life as if it were work. While such people may believe they play, exercise, dine, and make love, it's more accurate to say they work at playing, exercising, dining, and making love. To understand how this could be, consider a broad definition of what it means to work.

Symptoms *of* Work Fixation

The work-fixated person often:

- Values others as a function of their usefulness.
- May be insensitive to the feelings and working styles of others.
- Has a singular vision of how to get things done and is less likely to employ the shared visions and talents of team members.
- Is rational at the expense of intuition and feelings.

Colleagues of the work-fixated often feel:

- Used.
- Undervalued.
- That the fixated person has little sense of loyalty to them.
- A lack of connection to the fixated person.

People are at work whenever they intend to change the world from what it is to what they want it to be. At first glance, that may seem a bit odd, insofar as work is generally considered an activity, like caring for patients, writing a prescription, or digging a trench. The Dutch psychologist F.J.J. Buytendijk wrote that how we are present, rather than the activity itself, determines whether we're working, which explains why chopping wood or reading a book can be work for some but recreation for others. It all depends on our presence or intention as we approach and perform a task. At work, we have a plan and see the world as something to be used. When we're contemplative, we appreciate the world as it is.

Imagine a woman on a summer day picking flowers from her garden to bring indoors. She's looking for flowers with long stems and vibrant colors, and will likely leave behind those past their prime and those whose stems are too short for the vase she wants to use. This woman is a worker. She has a plan and views the garden as material for a bouquet. Now imagine that she has finished arranging the flowers and is sitting in a chair reading. For whatever reason, she looks up, the flowers catch her eye, and she stops. No words or thoughts are necessary. She simply notices their beauty, quietly and happily absorbing the image. That is a contemplative moment.

The person at work has a plan to change the world from the way it is (a flower bed) to the way she wants it to be (a bouquet). The flowers are raw material to be used rather than admired.

An outside observer might not notice anything unusual when work-fixated people are on the job. They seem to work well and others appreciate their contribution. The one way work-fixated people are noticed is if they run over co-workers, are insensitive to personal differences and work styles, and follow their own agenda, often at the expense of the team's shared vision.

In characterizing work fixation as an unhealthy work distortion, I'm not advocating less work so there's more time to live a balanced life. Rather, I'm setting the stage for recognizing work's value. Good hard work changes flowers into bouquets, helps heal the sick, transforms chemicals into medicines, and turns wool into garments. There is sacredness associated with what we do. Culture is fashioned and history is made as these activities transform the world. The goal is to work in less-fixated ways so we have a well-balanced relationship with work and thus healthier lives.

An unfortunate consequence for work-fixated people is that they miss the richness of life apart from work. For them, playing with children, loving, resting in awe before a breathtaking view, feeling a prayerful moment, taking a contemplative walk, or resting without self-reproach are relatively inaccessible experiences. Equally unfortunate, in pursuit of personal agendas the quality of their work suffers, and they harm co-workers and create tension in relationships. They may ultimately win in terms of achieving a goal, but they pay a terrible price: Deep personal emptiness and a trail of relationship destruction.

In contrast, when formerly work-fixated people have learned to stand appreciatively before the world as it is rather than the way they want it to be, how they work will change. What we experience away from work stays with us when we're back on the job. We need that time apart. We also need to be sure that activities away from work enliven rather than drain us. You may know a nurse or other co-worker who has just become a mother: She returns to work a markedly different person. The problem with fixation is that experiences outside of work—positive or negative, life-giving or life-draining—are lost and our lives overall lose depth and quality.

For health care providers, work fixation is particularly troubling because it's a huge roadblock to experiencing the full rewards of work. Instead of recognizing their value as a healing presence for others, providers easily slip into the mindset that their sole job is to do something for patients. In many ways that's true, whether it's making a diagnosis, administering the right medication, or bathing patients. Yet health care providers and caregivers are also obligated to be a healing presence. While no one wants to return to bygone days before the advent of modern medicine, there was a time when providers and caregivers could offer little more than their presence to advance the healing process. Physicians had few potions to administer; their presence and bedside manner were the sources of healing. Given the plethora of medicines today, providers may believe there's less need to bring a healing presence to patient care. If a hospital, nursing home, or medical office (or individuals or teams in one of these settings) diminishes or dismisses the value of healing presence, work fixation may be present.

In the popular movie *The Descendants*, George Clooney plays the role of a work-fixated husband and father who finally awakens to his life apart from work as his comatose wife lies dying in a hospital bed. With intense emotion and honesty, he says, "Good-bye Elizabeth, good-bye my life, good-bye my friend. My pain. My joy. Good-bye." These are the words of a man who has awakened to life beyond work.

The following exercise will help you learn from your life away from work. After you've completed it, we'll address work addiction.

Tip No. 5
to Help Ourselves

Learn *from* Your Life While *not at* Work

Review the description of work fixation and mark the words with which you agree and underline those with which you take issue. Be personal. There's no particular value in either agreeing or disagreeing with thoughts in this book. What's important is to formulate an understanding of how you work. Now, jot down some notes in response, to these questions:

• Has anyone told you that you seem unable to relax? Who were they? Do you agree? Disagree? Do you have another perspective?

- Do you approach playing, praying, biking, hiking or working out, spending time with your family, and other activities unrelated to your job as "work"? If you do, who besides you suffers as a result?

If you describe such activities as "work," think about what you may need to do to escape that trap. Try to be honest. No one ever needs to see what you write. Over time, becoming comfortable with life as it is rather than something that must be changed will yield considerable personal rewards.

THE BENEFIT TO YOU: Recognizing how work fixation may be present in the way you, your colleagues, department, staff, your spouse or partner works can be the beginning of learning a new way to work. The result? Joy, meaning and connecting presence—and improved patient care and satisfaction. Nice return on your investment of time. ໑

Work Addiction

Work-addicted individuals are driven to the point where they can't stop working even if they consciously try. The key word is "driven."

Most of us think of addiction as something that happens when people abuse substances such as cocaine, medications, tobacco, or alcohol. More accurately, addiction refers to a pathological relationship with a mood-altering substance, place,

Symptoms *of* Work Addiction

The work-addicted person often:

- Puts work before all other responsibilities (health and relationships).
- Works when not necessary and/or appropriate at the expense of other, more pressing priorities, such as those that involve being with family and friends.
- Uses the need-to-work as an explanation for frequent absences or abdication of other responsibilities.
- Maintains few personal relationships.

Colleagues of the work-addicted often feel that they can't help the addicted person and that the addict:

- Can't delegate. When he tries, his oversight is inappropriate.
- Is emotionally distant.
- Has work habits that have destroyed their working relationship.
- Is oblivious to and cut off from others.

or behavior. "Pathological" means that the relationship interferes with and takes precedence over all other relationships, including those we have with ourselves, loved ones, and work. An addict neglects any part of his or her life that gets in the way of or doesn't involve the addictive substance, place, or behavior. Although we've traditionally viewed addiction as a physiological dependence, psychological dependence can be every bit as strong.

To better understand some of the dynamics of work addiction, let's consider what we know about Bernard Madoff, the high-flying financier who is spending the final years of his life in prison for orchestrating a Ponzi scheme that defrauded institutional and individual investors out of billions of dollars. His wheelings and dealings ruined the financial security of many people. Madoff admitted he knew he was deceiving others, that what he was doing was morally wrong and illegal. Nevertheless, he didn't—and most likely couldn't—stop. People unfamiliar with the dynamics of addiction might say, "Surely Madoff could have stopped had he wanted to." In fact, something more than will power is necessary to lessen an addiction's death grip.

An addiction injures others and at the same time destroys the addict. Did Madoff enjoy ruining other lives? Probably not. Did he realize he would injure people, including his children and other loved ones, colleagues, and clients? Probably. However, as drug addicts know, that realization doesn't compare to the power and allure of the addictive source. Entirely self-absorbed, they think only in terms of that source and fulfilling the immediate need to continue experiencing the good feeling it delivers—the euphoria and relief of inner pain. Denial is a common symptom of addiction and a strong indicator of how important a substance or activity is to an addict. Denial and justification of the addictive behavior are protective devices that allow the behavior to continue unchecked.

Addictions often begin with overindulging in a satisfying activity that may be exciting, too, if only for a while. The same is true of work addiction, which frequently begins with the feeling of well-being that accompanies good, hard work. Then, the emerging work addict slips into wanting the feeling to endure and intensify. This feeling is immensely more satisfying than the emotional pain that otherwise haunts her.

Work- and substance-addicted people both suffer isolation and destroyed relationships as they often become alienated from children, spouses, and friends. Work offers temporary relief from other troubles. If there are difficulties at home, it provides a much needed and—here's the difference from other addictions—culturally sanctioned, almost socially acceptable escape.

One important difference between work-addicted and substance-addicted individuals is that the former seldom lose their jobs as a result of their behavior. Oftentimes, ironically, our culture and many health care systems reward work-driven behavior. Reward, along with denial and justification, allow the work addict to pursue his addiction with abandon.

The insights of former professional hockey star Ken Davies, an alcoholic in recovery before his death in 2004, are revealing. "When I was drinking," he once said, "the only control in my life was hockey. I wasn't drinking to relieve the stress of hockey; it was hockey that took the pressure off the rest of my life."[1,2] For Davies, work became a distorted way to cope with his personal life, which was out of control.

Such people are under the unrelenting influence of torturous, inescapable demons. They are successful on the job and rewarded accordingly but feel neither contentment nor peace, contrary to the way things may appear. At a meeting of the board of directors of a highly successful health care organization, I recall the CEO proudly referring to his management team as "hard-driving, Type A people. I don't want anyone on my team unless they are driven and impatient. I like people who can't relax." Pity the team members who weren't work-addicted.

The work-addicted are always in a hurry. It bothers them to watch others do things they know they can do faster. At a meeting, in a car, going to the movies, they become irritated when somebody or something gets in the way. They hurry others to finish speaking and even complete their sentences for them just so they can make a point. Indeed, two telltale signs of work addicts are their chronic sense of urgency and a competitive hostility. Little wonder they schedule more tasks and have increasingly less time do them, and that their hostility awakens fear in others. Work addicts' productivity and commitment may lead to job success, but they're certainly not models of healthy ways to work.

Most work-addicted people are comfortable working beside others like them. That's because addicts seek playmates to make their out-of-balance work habits seem normal or justifiable. They give each other a certain comfort level by setting a "new normal" of behavior, not unlike the alcoholic who seeks other alcoholics with which to drink.

Although people with more balanced lives can sometimes help the work-addicted, usually it's the non-addicted employees who suffer. If the workplace culture favors addiction, non-addicts are considered to be out of step. They're overlooked and sometimes devalued. If the boss gets to work at 6 a.m. and leaves at 8 or 9 p.m., colleagues may feel pressure to match those hours.

A common stereotype is that work addiction bedevils men rather than women. Marion Woolman, a highly experienced and well-respected psychoanalyst, thinks otherwise. Referring to some of her clients, she wrote:

Many [women] have proven beyond question that they are excellent doctors, excellent mechanics, excellent business consultants. But they are also, in many cases, unhappy women. "I have everything," they say. "Perfect job, perfect house, perfect clothes, so what? What does it all add up to? There's got to be more than this. I was born, I died, I never lived." Often, behind the scenes, they are chained to some addiction: food, alcohol, constant cleaning, perfectionism.[3]

What drives us to addiction? The answers are as many and varied as there are individuals. Disparate influences—power, fear, low self-esteem, perfectionism—drove Bernard Madoff, Ken Davies, and some of Marion Woolman's clients.

Do you have work-addiction tendencies? If so, writing in this book or journal will likely yield insight into why you work the way you do. After you complete the following exercises, we'll examine a third malady: Work exhaustion.

Recognize *the* Suffering *of* People *who are* Work-Addicted

Regarding the previous discussion of work addiction, write down what you agree with and what doesn't seem right. Try to be specific and give reasons why.

Now call to mind a colleague who strikes you as work-addicted. Imagine what it's like to be driven and unable to stop working, even if you want to. Write your thoughts about what she/he may feel. Then answer the following questions based on your own experience. Try to go beyond clichés or pat answers.

• Driven: What could be pushing her/him?

• Unable to stop: Why doesn't will power work?

• There never seems to be enough time: Can she/he ever relax?

• Work addiction hurts others: Who is she/he injuring? Finally, imagine you have an opportunity to talk with this addicted person—to demonstrate you really understand her/his suffering. Jot down how you think this conversation would go. This isn't the time to tell her/him what to do or to explain that you feel hurt, angry, or confused. Simply convey your empathetic understanding of how difficult these times must be for your colleague.

THE BENEFIT TO YOU: Recognizing work addiction in yourself or others is the first step toward compassion for the work addict and freedom from addiction. Reflection is a gift you give to yourself, allowing you to explore challenging topics and conditions that will lead to a breakthrough. ❧

Work Exhaustion

The third, often-praised malady is work exhaustion. This isn't the kind of fatigue associated with medical disorders such as fibromyalgia or chronic fatigue syndrome. Nor is it a form of depression. Rather, work exhaustion is the loss of spirit or heart. While these words are vague (some might say poetic), they are meaningful and powerful. As Joyce Carol Oates wrote, "The poetic figure of speech is a powerful one that no amount of scientific terminology and matter-of-fact discussions of serotonin deficiency, neurotransmitter systems, or tricyclics can match."[4]

"Exhaustion" comes from haust—the Latin word for "drawn," as in water taken out of a well—and ex- which is the equivalent of our English word "from." Thus, work exhaustion connotes having the last drop of water drawn from a person's depth. His well has run dry. He feels empty and dispirited. If you understand how someone can lose his spirit and still be in good health, you understand work exhaustion.

Consider the experiences of Amanda and Sasha, both of them critical care nurses in their mid-thirties, physically healthy, and psychologically balanced. A colleague described Amanda as "…a go-getter. She was our best advocate with administration. Somewhat playfully, but with some truth to it, we hoped she'd be our next manager. We liked her personable ways. I even heard one of the higher-ups talk about her as having senior management potential. But for the past year she's not been herself. She used to smile a lot and make really funny jokes. That energy has disappeared. I'd say she's doing OK, but not great. She seems more like someone going through the motions rather than being involved. She's lost her zip."

One of Sasha's colleagues said she "was one of our best critical care nurses. She was generous when she joined us out of school. You could ask her to do

Symptoms *of* Work Exhaustion

The work-exhausted person often:

- Appears lethargic.
- Exerts little effort to help themselves.
- Seems cold, uncaring, and detached.
- Complains about being tired.
- Is easily distracted and unable to complete tasks.

Colleagues of the work-exhausted often:

- Feel that the exhausted person is irritated or angered by the lethargy of others who are exhausted.
- Want to help, but nothing they do or suggest seems to work.
- Avoid exhausted people over time because they feel drained being around them.
- Feel that work-exhausted people diminish team or workplace morale.

anything and she'd bounce to it. She wouldn't just do it; she'd do it exceptionally well. I think she was one of the few nurses on the unit who would drop whatever she was doing to help patients whenever they pressed their call buttons. That was then, this is now. Today she's lethargic. She's still good at what she does and I'm glad she's on my team, but she's lost her bounce and is noticeably more cynical. I'd almost say that she has a wall around her. Before she was empathetic. Now she's cool and dispassionate, almost unfeeling. I wouldn't be surprised if she looks for another job or drops out of nursing. I don't know if she's just tired and needs a break or if she's simply become hardened by the job's nonstop demands. She's like many of us—tired of being generous."

I don't know anything about Amanda's and Sasha's families or social histories. However, co-workers tell us that both women were once engaged in their jobs and now appear withdrawn, that Amanda has lost her zip and Sasha her bounce. Although zip and bounce are immeasurable, the disappearance of these characteristics suggests that Amanda and Sasha are dispirited or uninspired. If we are work exhausted, we may neglect our spiritual side, which gets diminished or lost, just as we may neglect our physical or emotional health. For the work exhausted, the meaning of work slips away.

Remember, spirit isn't otherworldly, the exclusive domain of those who see themselves as spiritual, or the prerogative of people in communities of faith. If we accept the notion that, "Man is a body in the same degree that he is spirit, wholly body and wholly spirit,"[5] we understand there's a distinction between body and spirit, but they are inextricably woven together; the health of one impacts the health of the other. In this context, we view work fixation as a malady associated with body, work addiction as a disorder of the mind, and work exhaustion an affliction of spirit.

It's easy to picture Amanda and Sasha generously responding to the needs of patients and staff, given their generous natures. As critical care nurses at efficiently managed, high tech hospitals, they probably feel exceptional stress. Perhaps they manage the stress by being cool, detached, and mechanical—armor that encases their spirits and protects their hearts. The unintended consequence is that the two nurses are technically proficient but also distant and uncaring. Patients don't reap the benefits of Amanda's and Sasha's passion, compassion, and healing presence. And colleagues miss the human connection, support, and spirit that arise when fellow workers are fully engaged, lively, humorous, and enthusiastic.

Disillusionment is another symptom of work exhaustion. Who hasn't been excited about landing a meaningful job where co-workers were welcoming and energetic? For months or even years, all went well. Then a colleague retired, management changed, or the department was reorganized. Such changes can influence our attitude toward work. We may even begin to feel undervalued or relatively underpaid. Suddenly, a few changes in responsibilities or expectations cause once-meaningful work to lose its attraction. We see haggling and pettiness all around. Disillusionment sets in. Something seems to have disappeared and our heart is empty.

Betrayal can contribute to work exhaustion. I don't mean betrayal in the sense of bad faith, duplicity, or double-dealing, but rather situations in which highly talented, devoted, and generous employees extend or even overextend themselves for others and unrealistically expect to be rewarded for doing so. A manager recently laid off as a result of his hospital's reorganization told me, "I've worked here for 11 years. I'm as loyal as loyal can be. I've consistently worked more than expected, volunteered often, been selfless, and done everything as best I could. I've spent myself for this place. I gave it my all. Where is loyalty on their part?" Few experiences drain the heart more quickly. Resentment fills the void.

If you feel work exhausted, do you know why your heart has grown cold? Do you know how to help yourself?

Tip No. 7

to Help Ourselves

Describe *the* Experience *of* Work Exhaustion

- If you've experienced work exhaustion, write about what it feels like.

- If you haven't, describe what it's like to work with someone who is work exhausted. Be sure to describe their behaviors.

- In either Amanda's or Sasha's case, what might have led to their loss of spirit? Try not to ascribe this loss to a single factor. Let your mind be mischievously playful and curious as it explores the less obvious. You may learn something about yourself and others.

THE BENEFIT TO YOU: Work exhaustion—yours, your colleague's, or your supervisor's—has a profound impact on patient and employee satisfaction. As with other unhealthy work experiences, change begins with awareness. Identifying and exploring the underlying causes of work exhaustion can be an important first step in transforming lives and your work environment—one person at a time!

A Reflection

Very few employees within health care say they don't have enough to do. Most report they have too much on their plate and that the popular adage to do-more-with-less only adds to their stress. If you work in a clinic or physician practice, you surely know the rapid pace required to respond to patients' needs. While the pace of work within nursing homes tends to be slower, there is no way to reach the point that you can sit back and relax because you've done everything that needs to be done. There is always too much to do. Nowhere is this more evident than in large medical centers and hospitals.

Those who work in supportive roles to those who provide direct patient care also know the weight of long unfinished to-do lists. Ask anyone who works in Facilities, Administration, Finance or Quality. There are deadlines to be met, reports to submit and meetings to attend. Few are exempt from workplace pressures.

To handle the stress of too-much-to-do and too-little-time-to-do-it, researchers advise us to make a list of everything we need to do. Then, they say, take one of two approaches. The first approach is to prioritize our to-do list and then focus our energies only on the most important tasks.

The second approach is similar yet different in a significant way. Once the list is made, they tell us to cross off what we consciously decide not to do. That leaves us without a lingering list of unfinished work at the end of the day, though we have to live with the consequences of the decision, including people who are unhappy with our choice.

Perhaps there is a time and place for each approach or a combination of the two. Also, it is likely true that how we handle the problem of too-much-to-do varies with our differing temperaments and responsibilities. What we all share, however, is the struggle to live with the realization that the work of caring for others is never finished—just as we, as individuals, are unfinished.

Do you think that there is a connection between how we handle unfinished work and how we adjust to the challenge that we, too, are unfinished? If we think of ourselves as unfinished, do you think that attitude would help us when we're at work and caring for others? Jose Ortega y Gasset thought so. When thinking of all we must do, he reminded us: "Tell me to what you pay attention and I will tell you who you are."

What do you need to be particularly attentive to today? What do you need to decide not to do? ❤

Notes

Notes ~

Notes

Notes ⤳

4

Healing Unhealthy
Ways *of* Working

"The longest journey is
the journey inwards."

DAG HAMMARSKJÖLD, SWEDISH DIPLOMAT,

ECONOMIST, AND WRITER

There are steps you can take to reduce the grip that work fixation, work addiction, and work exhaustion have on your daily life. Some of the steps are simple, though not always easy. As you read in Chapter 3, we often adopt these distorted or unhealthy work behaviors as a result of early childhood experiences and coping methods. Change begins with awareness of these behaviors, but it must be followed by steady, consistent action: New behaviors that will lead to healthier ways to work and a more enriched, satisfying life.

Getting Work Fixation Under Control

Recall that work fixation is a way of living whereby someone approaches every activity with the mindset of a worker who intends to change the world from what it is to what she wants it to be. Whether the activity is playing, exercising, dining, or making love, it's just one more thing on a checklist of things to be accomplished rather than enjoyed simply for their own sake.

Getting this distorted, unhealthy behavior under control can be particularly challenging because work-fixated people are good employees and often highly successful. Their behavior and commitment to work are typically rewarded rather than questioned. Work-fixated individuals also appear to be normal; they seemingly play, have friends, parent their children, and even take vacations or pursue other interests. The problem is that such a person can only be present in the world by doing. So while their employer is happy, and everyone in this person's social network and larger community view her as a success and as someone to admire, she suffers because of her inability to truly appreciate life.

Work-fixated individuals are, as the cliché goes, human doings rather than human beings. Doing and being are the two fundamental, inseparable-yet-distinguishable sides of life. The distinction is that the doing side seeks to change life; the being side rests with the world as it is. Work-fixated doers can't rest contemplatively with the world as it is. An elk silently eating in a meadow at dusk, love between two persons, the understanding look shared by a patient and caregiver—these are lost on work-fixated doers. No amount of doing will yield, or open them up to, the secrets and immense sense of beauty and heightened spiritual awareness that the being side of life offers.

The difference between doing and being is especially pronounced in health care settings. For instance, a work-fixated nurse may approach a pediatric patient diagnostically; she knows what he needs medically and provides it. Another nurse, however, is awakened when she enters the room to find the child's mother tearfully comforting him. Touched, the nurse stands motionless and appreciatively so as not to interrupt that tender moment. The work-fixated nurse can't make the switch from doing to being.

Joseph Campbell, the mythologist, writer, and lecturer, said that the challenge facing many of us is how to "give up the life you planned in order to have the life that is waiting for you."[1a] For people who have learned to work at everything they do, giving up is not welcome advice.

The one time that work-fixated people realize they must live in more balanced ways is when there's a wake-up call or crisis. Four common ones are falling in love, illness, uncommon success, and failure.

Falling *in* Love

If you've worked with a dyed-in-the-wool, work-driven individual, you know firsthand how intense and focused such people are. They're usually oblivious to those around them. I know of a surgeon who became famous for his violent speech and action toward nurses at the hospital where he practiced. One time, the surgeon got so angry in the operating room, he threw an instrument at a nurse on his team. She immediately left, called the police, and accused him of assault. Believe it or not, he was arrested while leaving the OR in his scrubs.

Several months later, this surgeon fell in love with a wonderfully expressive, strong, clear-headed nurse who worked at a hospital across town. His behavior changed so radically, his friends and colleagues couldn't believe it. He expressed amazement that this woman loved him, that he no longer felt he had to excel at everything, that he felt satisfied with himself just as he was. His periodic outbursts of anger seemed to miraculously disappear. Others on his surgical team understandably remained skeptical of this transformation but acknowledged that the man seemed different. Their attitude was, "Let's see how long it lasts." In fact, it has lasted about two-and-a-half years.

Was it the call to police or his newly found love that changed him? We'll never know. Perhaps both played a role. Police intervention halted his unacceptable behavior. Being booked on and found guilty of assault was a wake-up call, and falling in love brought him back to himself. He later recalled, "When I think back to those days, I was a little crazy." The only word I'd disagree with is *little*; he was out of control. His license should have been suspended many years ago.

Philosophers often refer to the experience of falling in love as eros. Some psychologists think of it as infatuation. C.S. Lewis wrote that eros enters us "like an invader, taking over and reorganizing, one by one, the institutions of a conquered country,"[1] which describes the surgeon's experience. How else can one account for the fact that he takes dancing lessons with his new-found love, seems to be more sensitive to the feelings of others, has visited Chicago's museums for the first time, and has opted out of weekend calls from the emergency department to remain at home?

Illness

Illness can push people out of their work fixation, too. A well-documented example is Ignatius of Loyola, the 16th-century soldier and founder of the Jesuit Order who, in his younger years, was fixated on the work of soldiering. "He went about in the dress of a fighting man, wearing a breastplate and carrying a sword and other sorts of arms at all times," historians tell us.[1b] But at age 30, Ignatius of Loyola was seriously injured as an officer in the Spanish army and captured by the victorious

French. Evidently, Ignatius' captors so admired his courage that they released him and he returned to his hometown to recuperate. At home and weak from his injuries, there was nothing else for him to do but read, which spurred a lengthy process of self-examination that ultimately changed his world view and the way he lived. Illness shocked Ignatius out of his fixated ways. Consider the way he prayed: *"Take, O Lord, and receive my entire liberty, my memory, my understanding and my whole will. All that I am and all that I possess You have given me: I surrender it all to You to be disposed of according to Your will. Give me only Your love and Your grace; with these I will be rich enough, and will desire nothing more."*[2]

Of course, we don't live in the 16th century and many of us aren't Christian. Nevertheless, we can learn from Ignatius's experience. Just as illness caused Ignatius to relinquish his fixated ways, so it can change the way we perceive life, as the physician J.H. van den Berg clearly documented:

The woman who, while taking a bath, feels "a lump in her breast," puts away the soap and tells herself the terrifying message that death has entered her existence. The man who suffered from constipation for a few months and who hears the doctor say that a very serious operation is necessary sees the scenes of his life change...The beginning of every serious illness is a halt. Normal life is at an end. Another life takes its place, a life of a completely unknown nature. It is an experience of complete surprise, hardly imaginable to a healthy person.[3]

Such awakenings shake people from the comforts and sleepiness of everyday life, and catapult them from work fixation with such force that they reassess their values, review their priorities, and consciously take inventory of what they value in their lives.

Uncommon Success

"Nothing breeds success like success" is a familiar expression. But uncommon success also can awaken people who have viewed life only through the lens of work. Many of us believe that success is the magic pill, the solution to all our problems. If only we could achieve our dream through hard work, we'd live happily ever after. If we were successful, our lives would settle down, we'd relax and be loved, and our loneliness would subside.

Looking at so-called success stories, we discover that achieving success doesn't guarantee any of these side benefits. The American composer Irving Berlin certainly knew success. He also knew its demons. "The toughest thing about success," he said, "is that you've got to keep on being a success."[3a] The demons push and never let up. At some point, successful individuals ask themselves, "Do I want to keep this up? Is it worth the effort? Should I do something else?" Some muster the energy to press on. Others withdraw from life. Some awaken to the notion that their life's purpose may lie beyond the success they have achieved.

Consider the journey of a man—the son of a highly successful West Coast contractor—who jettisoned his fixated ways. He graduated from a prestigious university with a master's in business administration, then started a company to serve small organizations that wanted to outsource their monthly payment of bills. He was right in thinking that some churches and schools would welcome this service.

The business soon expanded to large nonprofit organizations, including sprawling hospital systems. It was so successful, the father thought his son might be doing something illegal. "You're making too much money too fast," he said. "Something must be wrong." The son welcomed an audit, which confirmed the new company's legitimacy and profit.

Not long afterward, he sold his business to become a venture capitalist. He was even more financially successful than before. Three years after that, to the surprise of many, he sold this company, too, and established a foundation to aid the economically disadvantaged in his city. Then he showed up on the doorstep of a monastery with the intent of becoming a monk, which shocked his family and everyone else who knew him, including me. He's still there, some 29 years later.

What prompted him to enter a monastery at age 45? Had he done something terribly wrong and tried to hide? Wouldn't it have been better if, based on his financial success, he had contributed even more to the economically disadvantaged people of the world? His thinking went something like this:

"There was a time that I believed in what I was doing. That belief kept me going. But once I was successful, everything changed. It was as if my view of life changed. When that happened, whatever kept me interested in building a company lost its hold. I don't know if this is true for anyone else, but I can now see that I was riveted on success. I was oblivious to everything that didn't help me get there. I guess you'd say I wore blinders."

I'd say he exhibited the behavior of a fixated worker. While he was pleasant, engaging, and even charming around others, he had no significant relationships and few interests apart from work. But "once I was successful, everything changed," he explained. Uncommon success led this man to come home to himself, a transformation that marvels me to this day. Although he's still interested in the financial world (the monastery's finances are his responsibility), he's immensely more relaxed and able to enjoy a variety of leisure interests. "Sitting in the silence of prayer each morning and evening is something I relish," he said.

When work-fixated people see the falsehoods of their thinking and success no longer holds the same allure, they have an opportunity to re-evaluate such thinking, values, and the way they've been living.

Failure

Lack of success, defeat, disillusionment. Call it what you will, failure—particularly significant failures—can push people out of their work fixation. It forces critical self-evaluation and an admission that something they're doing isn't quite right.

Management professors use stories of failure to illustrate how the experience is often a catalyst for later success. School children learn that Abraham Lincoln overcame electoral losses before he succeeded. Jeffrey Immelt, the successful CEO of General Electric, one of the world's largest corporations, tells GE's senior leaders, "Surviving a failure gives you more self-confidence. Failures are great learning tools."[3b] Legendary baseball slugger Babe Ruth knew in his bones that fear of failure was a demon. "Never be afraid to strike out," he advised.

These wise words extol the virtue of hard work, determination, and perseverance. But there's more: Failure also is an opportunity to awaken from the drowsiness of everyday life. Nowhere is this more dramatically illustrated than in the archetypal story of Adam and Eve. Recall that they blissfully went about their lives in the Garden of Eden, unaware of being naked. When Adam and Eve failed to live up to their commitment and ate the forbidden fruit, they became conscious of their nakedness and covered themselves. They awoke to life.

J.K. Rowling, the now-famous author of the extraordinarily popular and best-selling Harry Potter series, has known failure. She experienced lingering clinical depression, a failed marriage, extreme poverty, and publishers' many rejections of her manuscripts. What could be more crippling? Yet, when she was depressed, sometimes severely so, failure made her realize that irrational fear hindered her work and kept her from enjoying life.

Failure was the theme of her 2008 commencement address to Harvard University students. She reflected that if she hadn't experienced and faced failure head on, she wouldn't have pursued the only work she'd ever dreamed of doing. By hitting a failure-induced bottom, she realized she had nothing to lose, became grateful for the life she had, and began to write her one big idea. Through failure, self-knowledge and self-confidence bloomed, and resilience and courage surfaced to allow her to resurrect her life and follow her dream. Failure gave her life-long gifts that she couldn't have received any other way.

When a person's work-fixated world collapses, he has an opportunity to follow Rowling's example and stop pretending to be anyone other than himself. That seemingly mundane insight helped Rowling direct her energies into finishing the only work that mattered. In a manner of speaking, failure enabled Rowling to regain herself.

Falling in love, illness, uncommon success, and failure are just some of the major events that may trigger changes in work-fixated behavior. Others are the death of a loved one and awareness of aging. Whatever the trigger, it's an opportunity to discover a new and refreshed life.

Engage *in* Competitive Play

Tip No. 8

to Help Ourselves

Absent illness or failure, one thing you can actively do to escape work fixation is engage in competitive play. Sports such as soccer, baseball, and tennis, and even poker, bridge, and chess, get the competitive juices flowing. The sensation and exhilaration of competition are starkly different from the driven, heavy feelings that characterize work fixation. They shake us up, open the door to recognition of our distorted, unhealthy work behavior, and motivate us to move beyond it.

Losing a game can be a moment of grace because the feeling it generates contrasts in a healthy way with the feeling at work that we must always succeed and be in control. Even experiencing the disappointment of losing an inconsequential game of chess or bridge can create a chink in our armor that will open us to examining our work-fixated approach to life. Engaging in a competitive game is a safe opportunity to expose oneself to an initially uncomfortable side of life where vulnerability is a gift rather than something to be avoided. When a work-fixated person loses a game, his sense of invincibility is shattered and he opens up to more heart-based feelings of love, empathy, and affection, as well as an understanding and appreciation of himself and others.

In these journal pages, note your feelings of depression, unhappiness, disappointment, or some other ways you've felt after losing a competition:

- Has anyone ever directly or indirectly suggested that you need to be in control?

- How do you shield yourself from failure?

- Name some instances in which you experienced failure, then reflect on and write about what you have learned from each one.

Remember, the notes you make in this journal are your private thoughts that you don't need to share with anyone else.

THE BENEFIT TO YOU: Experiencing failure as insignificant as losing a game of tennis can create a vulnerability that will open our hearts and minds to examining our work-fixated way of life. What are the rewards for this self-examination? Appreciating the "being" side of life which creates more meaning and peace in our world and ultimately, more heart-connected interactions with our coworkers, patients and their families. ✍

Tip No. 9
to Help Ourselves

Create Situations *that* Make You Feel Vulnerable

Many people who live in fixated ways feel particularly vulnerable. They guard against this vulnerability by erecting a virtually impenetrable wall and insisting they maintain a sense of control over their lives. For the wall to be penetrated, work-fixated individuals must create situations that force them to face their vulnerabilities. Otherwise, why should they go to the trouble of changing?

Situations that cause anxiety in one person don't necessarily affect another person; they are as varied as the people experiencing the anxiety. There are numerous ways to stir up the pot—to create enough anxiety to force a review of the dissatisfaction or unhappiness in our lives and how we work. Anxious moments are those that give us sweaty palms or even a thrill. For example, some people feel vulnerable when they are intimate with others. Opening up to being loved awakens the possibility of being hurt. C.S. Lewis could have been describing work-fixated individuals when he wrote about those who fear loving or being loved.

"To love at all is to be vulnerable. Love anything, and your heart will certainly be wrung and possibly broken. If you want to make sure of keeping it intact, you must give your heart to no one, not even to an animal.

Wrap it carefully round with hobbies and little luxuries; avoid all entan-glements; lock it up safe in the casket or coffin of your selfishness. It will become unbreakable, impenetrable, irredeemable. "[4]

In these journaling pages, jot down a list of situations at home and work that make you feel especially vulnerable. Think of as many as possible. Then, for each one, write about the vulnerability you feel and why. Answer the question: "What could happen to me if I'm not careful?"

After you've finished, mark those situations for which you think your fears are well-founded and respond to these questions:

- How likely is it that the feared outcome will happen?

- What if it does? Can I handle the consequences?

- Would it have been helpful to expose my vulnerability in each case?

Finally, reflect on situations in which it would be helpful to reveal your vulnerability and push through your anxiety, and how you might do that. Work-fixated individuals will identify many of these. You may want to commit yourself to creating more opportunities for vulnerability, lead with your heart, and connect in a more loving, authentic way with others.

THE BENEFIT TO YOU: Facing our fears and understanding our anxieties can free us to pursue our deepest desires. Why not go for it? All you have to lose is the fear that's holding you back from being your best and achieving your dreams! ↶

Take Contemplative Walks

Tip No. 10

to Help Ourselves

A slow, contemplative walk is nothing more than a stroll without purpose. It is not undertaken for exercise, to awaken creativity, or to calm oneself. Work-fixated people who take contemplative walks are expressing a willingness to do something purposeless, which may break fixation's hold on them. There's a chance that this activity will invite them to be more reflective and live in the present moment.

Where you stroll isn't important. Intention is. A long corridor will do. If you live in the city, a walk around block is just fine. You just need a little time and a commitment to take frequent, contemplative walks—maybe one a day, at least for a while. The best walks don't require any thinking (no worries about traffic, for example) and are deliberately aimless. Mazes, labyrinths, botanical gardens, woods, a path along the lakeshore, and other peaceful, natural settings are especially suitable for contemplative walks.

While you're walking, don't be surprised if thoughts such as these come to mind: "I realize my world is really narrow," "there is a whole part of me that is undeveloped," or "I have a problem." Insight alone won't enable you to break free of a work-distorted behavior, but it is a gift that will help you begin moving in a new direction. The perk linked with taking a walk is that you'll have snippets of time to be with yourself—an inner vacation of sorts.

THE BENEFIT TO YOU: This is an easy, immediate and healthy activity that you can start right now! If you are breaking a pattern of work fixation, it's better not to have an outcome, destination or goal in mind. Just wander and see where you end up! ∽

Getting Work Addiction Under Control

Work fixation is the most difficult of the unhealthy work behaviors to overcome. That's because most work-fixated individuals are high functioning, extremely successful, able to accomplish things, and tend to deny that there's anything wrong with the way they work. On the other hand, work addiction is far easier to address and control but still requires a degree of focus and commitment.

An element that contributes to the difficulty of overcoming a work addiction is the enabling that can exist in the work environment. Work-addicted individuals tend to determine the culture of a workplace more forcefully than those who work in balanced ways. They may be rewarded with bonuses and promotions for their work achievements—until they begin to suffer the negative consequences of this addictive work style, that is. While work-addicted individuals are sometimes helped by workers who have a more balanced work style, more often than not it is the non-addicted employees that suffer. If the culture of the workplace favors the addicted worker, those who are more work-balanced are the ones who are considered out of step, overlooked, and sometimes devalued.

Ultimately, despite any workplace enabling, work-addicted people, unlike those who are work-fixated, may reach a point where the harmful or uncomfortable consequences of their unhealthy, distorted behavior far outweigh its advantages. There's a motivation to change behavior if for no other reason than to reduce those negative consequences.

An addiction to work, gambling, or sex is as toxic as having an unhealthy, consuming relationship with a drug or alcohol. Just as withdrawal from substance addiction entails severe physical symptoms, the angst of moving away from a behavioral addiction can be equally difficult and generate harsh emotional and spiritual pain. Because of the destructive, imbalanced behaviors that drive the addicted person, addictions ultimately lead to broken relationships and poor health.

External pressure from family, friends, and society may contribute to addictive behavior, but addicts are driven from within. Despite their good intentions, they can't stop what they're doing. Getting addiction under control requires an event, person, or realization—or all three—that is more influential than whatever drives the addict toward self-destructive behavior.

There's no cure for any kind of addiction—including work addiction. At Alcoholics Anonymous meetings, attendees typically introduce themselves with words like, "Hi, my name is _____ and I'm an alcoholic. I've been sober for 21 years." Embedded in those words is the recognition that years of sobriety are no guarantee of continued sobriety—that just beneath the surface, addictive tendencies are alive and well. What ensures sobriety is the decision in this moment to remain sober rather than fall back into self-defeating behaviors.

Most work-addicted people don't seek help until they are forced, either by an internal crisis or external forces, to change their life somehow. Three typical forces are: physical illness, an inability to sustain significant relationships, and dissatisfaction with oneself. If an addict is ill, he simply can't continue working as he did. If his relationships with loved ones end in failure, he may consider that his behavior was the cause. Debilitating self-doubt, crushing self-dissatisfaction, and personal suffering can be so overwhelming, change is the only option. Whatever leads people to relinquish their addiction, it's a gift, though it hardly seems so at the time. They may feel despair and isolation, and realize they can't recover alone. They need the help of others who have hit similar lows. The most important decision they can make is to join a support group.

Join *a* Support Group

Tip No. 11

to Help Ourselves

Support groups are necessary and effective because all members know the experience of being driven and unable to control their behavior. They soon realize that others who have escaped work addiction understand their suffering in a way that most people don't, and can help them understand and accept this unhealthy, distorted thinking and behavior.

Among formal support groups, Workaholics Anonymous is one of the best. Although WA is a worldwide organization that hosts meetings in most states, not every city has a chapter. Its Web site (www.workaholics-anonymous.org) has links to a variety of printed materials, including the W.A. Book of Recovery, a treasure chest of information.

Importantly, overcoming work addiction is more than acquiring knowledge. It involves continual surrender—a phrase that's easy to voice but a challenge to live—and taking each day and each event one at time.

Informal support groups composed of friends or colleagues can also help. The more effective ones include members who've overcome their work addiction. A group's impact will be negligible or even harmful if it merely affirms and emotionally supports members without helping them recognize their self-defeating rationalizations.

THE BENEFIT TO YOU: For relief from work addiction, borrow from the successful approaches used to overcome other addictions. Support groups help us create connections and learn from one another. By joining a group of people who share a common goal, we grow in self awareness and compassion and make friends at the same time. We don't have to do it alone. ↝

Seek Professional Help

Tip No. 12

to Help Ourselves

Psychotherapy and counseling can help work-addicted people through the sometimes painful and shocking rollercoaster process of self-discovery after they've scaled back to a more balanced and moderate routine for awhile. Professional guidance provides insight into why we work in addictive ways.

Recovering alcoholics know they must dig deeper into the underlying causes and conditions that resulted in their addictive behavior. This work will last a lifetime. Even those who've been sober for many years continually peel away layers of denial when they ask themselves what led them to drink. The answers are many and will change and become more insightful and nuanced over time. Becoming more fully awakened to the "why" of their addictive patterns can be very distressing—almost as stressful as the path they took to achieve abstinence, but very rewarding.

There is a difference between psychotherapy and counseling. Psychotherapy involves a professional relationship with the focus almost exclusively on the person seeking help. With effective psychotherapy, the client will learn little if anything about the therapist's life, but she will learn a lot about herself.

Counseling, in contrast, is a highly specialized and informed conversation between a wise and highly trained professional and the client, whose goal is to gain awareness and understanding of her addictive behaviors. However, the process is different than in the psychotherapeutic approach. With counseling, there tends to be more give-and-take between counselor and client than there is in a relationship with a psychotherapist. Often the counselor will be a little more self-revealing and may even make suggestions and recommend actions.

Most people begin with counseling rather than psychotherapy. Perhaps that is because the counseling relationship more closely resembles a healthy relationship between two persons. Over time, with a new trust in themselves, they may engage in formal psychotherapy, which is usually an unsettling journey. However, as painful as the inward journey may be, it offers the possibility of self-understanding, self-respect, and inner peace.

THE BENEFIT TO YOU: By creating a network at work of people who share your goal of overcoming work addiction, you form an immediate support system and forge deep ties with colleagues.

You're never alone and help is as close as a text, call or coffee break meeting. ℘

Tip No. 13
to Help Ourselves

Accept Support *from* Work-Sober Colleagues

Find support from work-sober people who are free from their addiction and recognize the seductive thinking and games that are common among addicts. Only work-sober colleagues can offer the kind of real-life, credible support and affection you need.

Everyone, including work-addicted individuals, needs the support of friends and loved ones; but asking for help can sometimes be daunting, particularly for people who feel they can overcome their addiction on their own.

This suggestion also is difficult to follow because it often puts a strain on others, particularly loved ones. Here's a real life example: The Vice President of Human Resources of a small rural hospital met regularly with others who were struggling to overcome their addiction to work. His wife was grateful for the changes he was making and delighted with the fact that he was spending more time with their children. "I'm delighted with what's happened to Jack. To tell you the truth, he is changing and he's at home with the kids in a way he never was before. If there's a problem, it's that he doesn't talk to me the way I wish he would. The way he tells it, it's easier for him to talk with his Monday night group. I wish he'd talk to me more. It's not that I think he is having an affair or something. I just resent the fact that he feels they understand him more than I do."

Work sobriety is changing this couple's relationship; it is not destroying their marriage. However, work sobriety creates an opportunity for them to connect with each other in new ways. It will require patience and adjustment on everyone within the family as he begins to live a more balanced life.

THE BENEFIT TO YOU: Addiction is a lonely path to travel. Recovering from addiction is easier with the support of others. Connecting with others at work who share a vision of a healthier, more enriching work life will make achieving this vision more likely. ᎒

Getting Work Exhaustion Under Control

Work exhaustion results when people lose heart or spirit in the workplace, a loss that spills over into their personal life. The challenge for work-exhausted individuals is to either reignite their energy and enthusiasm or move on to other employment. Those of us in health care who want to get this distorted, unhealthy work behavior under control should recall the inner fire they brought with them into their profession, rather than focus on the web of job-related forces that caused them to feel so drained. That inner fire is love—not sentimentality about the good ol' days, but a kind of love that "begins with paying attention to others, with an act of gracious self-forgetting," as John O'Donohue, the poet, philosopher, and scholar, put it in his book *Anam Cara: A Book of Celtic Wisdom.* He also wrote:

"You can be very successful in this world, be admired by everyone, have endless possessions, a lovely family, success in your work, and have everything the world can give, but behind it all, you can be completely lost and miserable. If you have everything the world has to offer you, but you do not have love, then you are the poorest of the poorest of the poor. Every human heart hungers for love. If you do not have the warmth of love in your heart, there is no possibility of real celebration and enjoyment. No matter how hard, competent, self-assured, or respected you are, no matter what you think of yourself or what others think of you, the one thing you deeply long for is love. No matter where we are, who we are, what we are, or what kind of journey we are on, we all need love."[5]

Work exhaustion is especially challenging for health care professionals because their work is unique. Patients' needs are seemingly unending and frequently urgent, and their fragile physical condition often adds a layer of desperation, fear, and anger to every request for assistance. Workers are sensitive to those needs and reach out in generous and selfless ways. That's love. The problem is, they sometimes forget how to be as generous toward themselves. They aren't as quick to cater to their own need for a break or to acknowledge a job well done.

If work exhaustion takes hold in your life, you're unable to brush off a colleague's chance remark that seems hurtful, or perhaps you dredge up a long-ago betrayal that ferments into full-blown resentment. This piling on of hurt can dampen and eventually wear down anyone's spirit.

One way for those in health care to fan rather than extinguish the flame within their hearts is by remembering to also care for themselves. As the Dalai Lama is said have commented, "In dealing with those who are undergoing great suffering, if you feel 'burnout' setting in, if you feel demoralized and exhausted, it is best for the sake of everyone to withdraw and restore yourself."[6a]

The country songwriter and singer John T. Morris got it right: "You were made to be a sailor, but you're a country boy. /Made to be a tailor, but you can't find your joy. /Made to be a singer, but you can't find your song./Maybe it's time to move along."[6b]

Work exhaustion can be an opening that leads to personal growth. Carl Jung remarked that when people finally attain the job or social standing they sought in the first stage of their lives, they inevitably ask, "Has it been worth it?" "Is this what I want?" They realize they "cannot live the afternoon of life according to the program of life's morning—for what was great in the morning will be little at evening, and what in the morning was true will at evening have become a lie."[7]

Self-questioning may lead work-exhausted individuals to seek employment elsewhere or even change careers altogether. Others may stay the course and try to muster the energy to push on. In either case, relief will only come if they make inner changes.

Many people think of work as a curse, a necessary evil. You'll hear them say that if they didn't have to work, they wouldn't. But others don't see it that way. In virtually every industry and profession, there are people who find their work energizing, fulfilling and even fun. According to Colleen Barrett, President of Southwest Airlines, "Work is either fun or drudgery. It depends on your attitude. I like fun."[7a] Pablo Picasso relished working in his studio. "When I work I relax; doing nothing or entertaining visitors makes me tired,"[7b] he said. Monks are well known for experiencing their work as a prayer.

How we view ourselves, our work, and our relationships shapes our life experience. The story of masons building a cathedral in the Middle Ages illustrates how our frame of reference can vary:

"What are you doing?" an observer asks one of them.

"I'm cutting stones," he replies.

The observer asks another mason, "What are you doing?"

His response: "I'm building a cathedral."

This difference in perspective applies to us, too. Our work

can stay the same or change dramatically if we alter our perspective and approach to it. Tip No. 14 will help you clarify your attitude toward work. After you've finished, turn to page 160 for another example illustrating the importance of perspective.

Clarify Your Attitude *toward* Work

Tip No. 14

to Help Ourselves

What mindset do you bring to work? Be inquisitive. Using these journaling pages, copy any of the following that apply to you. Feel free to add others not on the list. Work is:

- A career.
- A calling.
- Having a profession.
- An occupation.
- A duty.

- A necessity.
- A job.
- Punishment.
- A way to get ahead.

Here are some real-life examples of work-related mindsets and facts, and possible antidotes:

MINDSET: "Nursing is a career."

FACT: "I've lost interest in being a nurse."

RE-IMAGINING: "Is there only one way to be a nurse?"

• • •

MINDSET: "Work is a necessity. I have to work; I need the money."

FACT: "Work is boring."

RE-IMAGINING: "If I followed my dream, would money follow?"

• • •

MINDSET: "Work is a calling. I feel called to serve the elderly."

FACT: "I'm really tired."

RE-IMAGINING: "Are there other jobs that serve the elderly?"

• • •

MINDSET: "Work is a job."

FACT: "I've never been able to find the right job."

RE-IMAGINING: "Is something being asked of me in my life and career?"

• • •

MINDSET: "Accounting is a profession."

FACT: "Everything about accounting is boring and routine."

RE-IMAGINING: "Is it possible to change professions?"

• • •

MINDSET: "Work is always a drag."

FACT: "I don't like work and I wish I didn't have to work."

RE-IMAGINING: "Is there a job I would do even if I weren't paid?"

• • •

MINDSET: "Work is an occupation. I'm stuck with it."

FACT: "I'll work wherever I can find a job."

RE-IMAGINING: "Is it possible to establish a work identity I can take from one job to another?"

• • •

MINDSET: "Work is a way to get ahead in life."

FACT: "I've done well, ahead of many others, but I'm restless."

RE-IMAGINING: "What am I trying to achieve?"

• • •

MINDSET: "I have to accept my role to stay home and care for my ailing parents."

FACT: "I'm depressed."

RE-IMAGINING: "I need to coordinate my parents' care, not provide it."

• • •

To reap the greatest rewards from this activity, write clearly and succinctly about your current, work-related mindset and the one you want to develop.

THE BENEFIT TO YOU: By understanding your perspective on work, you can see how your attitude fuels or drains your passion and energy at work. This exercise offers alternative perspectives to try on as an antidote to holding on to an attitude that fosters work exhaustion—a condition that depletes your spirit and negatively influences your colleagues. ☙

How people interpret this painting by Wes Madgar, is a dramatic example of perspective. What do you see and feel? What's the man doing? Do you like the painting as art? Why or why not? Here's what four others wrote about their impressions:

A nurse: "I don't like the painting at all. Too drab. It makes me feel gloomy. It paints a negative picture of big city life and all those who work in these immense gray buildings behind him. The man probably has a cubicle desk in one of them."

A chief financial officer: "Sometimes I feel like the man in the painting. He's trying to quench his thirst with gutter water. I guess you can find relief anywhere but the gutter is a risky place. The painting makes me feel sorry for those who have to work in sterile settings."

A physician: "Depressing. Poor art. The painter made the man's head too big. It's illustrating the drabness of city life in a technological world. I don't like it. I don't feel this way about the city and I don't need to drink out of the gutter."

A business manager: "Is a print available online? I like it. The guy is cherishing water. If I were naming the painting, I would call it 'Oasis.' It reminds me of the time I was in Afghanistan and dehydrated. That's when I learned that water, like so many things we overlook, is precious."

Clearly, how we view the world, including the world of work, influences what we see, reflects our values, shapes our mood, and directs how we go about our day. Think of those days when you're in an upbeat mood and you view work as a safe place where good things happen. You're likely to assume the best of intentions in colleagues' emails, at meetings, and in all encounters. Conversely, when you're feeling drained, negative interpretations of every interaction and event abound, accumulate and weigh you down until it becomes unbearable.

No one has to tell us we're work exhausted; we can feel it in our heart and soul. Even though we rest enough, we feel drained of energy. However, a characteristic sense of deflation, of inner deadness, may not be enough to grab our attention. That might require physical illness or an inexplicable slowing down, as our bodies begin to rebel. Some self-examination will reveal that the source of our malaise is spiritual or emotional, not physical.

As people look for the underlying cause of their deep dissatisfaction with work, it's not unusual for them to blame others or themselves. But, as they soon learn, blaming others doesn't help. It simply keeps them stuck. There's no progress unless they focus on what they can do to change the situation or themselves.

Tackling the issues that lead to work exhaustion is a matter of the heart, and awareness is the first step in opening up to and healing the heart. By heeding previous tips in this book, you've already begun to listen to your heart and awaken to its desires. Writing down your thoughts is an extremely helpful way to regain a connection to our wise inner voice, but it can't replace learning from and connecting with others, particularly a spiritual director or coach.

Spiritual direction is a discipline that helps people in their search for meaning—what's asked of them in life—rather than what is personally satisfying. Spiritual directors or coaches are helpful in this process. You will likely benefit from spiritual direction if you are framing your concerns in the form of a question such as, "What does God ask of me?"

There are both highly trained professionals and well-intentioned but uninformed practitioners who identify with being spiritual directors. Consequently it is important to seek those who are knowledgeable and respectful of your spiritual or religious traditions. Qualified individuals usually have masters degrees or doctorates in divinity from accredited academic institutions.

Searching professional associations is one way to find qualified professionals. For example, Spiritual Directors International is a global learning community of people from many faiths and many nations who share a common concern, passion and commitment to the art and contemplative practice of spiritual direction. Their website offers a clear description of spiritual direction as well as a guide on how to find a spiritual director. There are links explaining the unique character of spiritual direction within differing traditions: Christian, Jewish, Islamic, Buddhist, Taoist and Eastern-philosophy (yoga).

In contrast to spiritual direction, coaching involves an ongoing relationship with an experienced professional who knows the world of work. A coach helps her client work in a more balanced way that will prevent work exhaustion. Expect the coach to be practical and directive.

Although no scientific studies have documented the effectiveness of spiritual direction and coaching, there is considerable anecdotal evidence that each approach is effective and valuable. Both can help us avoid work exhaustion. Choose the one that is appropriate for you (see Tip No. 15).

Tip No. 15
to Help Ourselves

Seek Spiritual Direction, Psychotherapy *or* Coaching

For help in deciding which type of guidance is right for you, reflect in these journal pages on the following questions:

- Have I been feeling down? If yes, did I just start feeling this way?

- Can I remember the time when I started feeling down?

- Have I felt a little depressed for years?

- Was there something or someone who triggered these feelings?

- Have I had a medical/physical exam recently, and if so, did the subject of depression come up?

- Do I feel healthy?

- Realistically, do I have the ability and energy to do what ever I need to do to find meaningful employment? If not, what gets in my way?

- Are others living my life for me? If so, who are they?

- Is there anything in my life apart from work about which I am concerned?

- Everyone has responsibilities to loved ones, oneself, and the job. What are mine?

- Which responsibilities are enjoyable? Which ones do I struggle with?

- Have I chosen my responsibilities or are they unavoidable?

- Do I think of myself as a spiritual person?

- Am I a religious person?

- Do I live my life according to a moral code I've adopted?

- Am I uncomfortable with religious or spiritual talk?

- Have I had an experience of God (G-d, Supreme Being, Universe, Allah, etc.] in my life?

- Is it important for work to feel spiritually meaningful and like a calling?

Finally, reflect on this quote by Viktor Frankl, the philosopher and author: *"Everyone has his own specific vocation or mission in life; everyone must carry out a concrete assignment that demands fulfillment. Therein he cannot be replaced, nor can his life be repeated, thus, everyone's task is as unique as his specific opportunity."*[8] Is this how you feel?

How do you decide the most appropriate kind of help for you? Consider these general thoughts:

1. When you're feeling troubled, consult a physician to either diagnose or rule out a medical condition.

2. If you are having difficulty coping with the challenges of life and you know that you need help, seek either psychotherapy or counseling.

3. If, after consultation or psychotherapy, you wish to seek help to awaken to the mystery of the sacred in life, then consider spiritual direction.

4. Seek out a coach if you feel that you would benefit from talking with someone who shares similar experiences, has insight, and can offer wise and periodic advice.

Whether you choose psychotherapy, spiritual direction or coaching, use the entries in these journal pages to focus your sessions—to jog your memory and trigger conversation. You can do this while protecting the privacy of your writing in these journaling pages.

THE BENEFIT TO YOU: Answering these questions will give you a snapshot of your emotional and spiritual health. If you're depressed or down, you might want to consider outside professional help. The questions in Tip No. 15 will help you determine if you would benefit most from a spiritual director, coach or psychotherapist. ❧

Case Study

BEING HONEST ABOUT WHAT WE NEED

A nurse reported this insight to her coach:

"I've gained real expertise in developing programs to help diabetic patients control their diet. I love doing it. I like it better than working on the floor over in the hospital.

"Three years ago, a clinic across town asked me to help them develop a similar program. I was flattered. Then the clinic director of that facility invited me to make a presentation at a symposium she was organizing. That, too, was fun. Slowly, I guess I made a name for myself and began to get invitations to speak around the state. The director at my place seemed to like the attention the clinic was getting. Last week, I led a panel during a general session of the state's diabetic association.

"I don't know if you know what nursing is like, but it's frenzied and tiring, particularly as you get older. Getting away to give these talks helped me keep perspective. I liked the change of pace and being thought of as something of an expert. What I never told anyone was that I would schedule an extra day away from the clinic on both ends of the presentation. It was one way I could take time for myself.

"That was my modus operandi for almost two years. It all changed when I accepted an invitation to speak at a meeting in Chicago. What I didn't realize was that my director registered for the same conference. I realized that once she looked over the program, she would know I had submitted paperwork requesting five days away from the clinic even though I really only needed three.

"I was embarrassed and anxious. What would she think? I was so upset that I went to my friend, the office manager, and asked what she thought I should do. I knew she would keep a confidence. Here's what she said:

"'Janet, you've got a problem. It's not that you've been dishonest. You're just afraid to be yourself. I know the director well. If you walked into her office and said that you needed an extra day or two for yourself because you were feeling blah or that you were losing your creativity, she'd probably hug you and OK the extra days away. She may even give you a few bucks for a drink! Don't you think she'd rather have someone who is alive and creative on her staff than someone who mopes around and is depressed or, worse still, negative?'

"I haven't forgotten that advice and have changed the way I handle the extra days I add on to my presentations. When I told my director, she didn't hug me, but she's been as supportive as anyone could be."

YOUR INSIGHT:

_____

_____

_____

_____

_____

LESSON: In some work cultures, people mistakenly think they must hide activities for taking care of themselves. If they were honest about their self care needs, they would feel supported, not burdened by them.

A Reflection

HUMAN ERRORS

Many have heard of Julie Thao, RN. She is the highly experienced and competent nurse who mistakenly administered the wrong medication to a young mother that resulted in the patient's death. Today, almost every hospital, nursing home and medical office is understandably obsessed with efforts to provide safe care because they know that human errors harm patients.

Rather than hide or deny human errors or blame or punish those who make them, we now know that patient safety is a multifaceted issue. It involves focused leadership, the use of effective technologies, the recognition of system issues that lead to errors, and the self care of individual providers. Surprisingly, the need to care for ourselves is often overlooked.

Why is that? You would think that those of us who spend our lives caring for others would be certain to care for ourselves. Evidently, that is not necessarily the case. Julie Thao volunteered to work a second shift even though she was so tired at the end of the first shift, she tried to rest in an empty patient's room before beginning her second shift. It was on that second shift that the medication error occurred. As generous as she was—and as so many of us are—does the effort to be generous by volunteering for a second shift trump the need to care for ourselves?

Some believe that we must care for ourselves before we care for others. After all, they say, remember the flight attendant's safety procedures announcement for passengers: "Put your mask on before helping your child." The reasons are evident.

Others recognize the value of being generous. They point to the nearly universal admiration we have of people willing to sacrifice themselves for others. Seldom, they say, does tragedy follow when we are in the act of doing something for others.

One nurse told me that the distinction is misleading. She insisted that we needed to care for ourselves and be generous. "The two are inseparable," she said. "Put generosity before self care and you end up with what happened to Julie. Put self care before generosity and you breed a bunch of individualists who can't work as a team."

What do you think? What has your experience taught you? How do others on your team handle this issue? ❧

Notes ∾

Notes ⌐

Notes �

Notes

Overwork: Causes
and Consequences

"Here lies Jeremy Brown,

born a man and died a grocer."

EPITAPH ON A LONDON TOMBSTONE

Work fixation, addiction, and exhaustion lead to overwork—
working too hard and too long. Overwork is a manifestation of
a life out of balance. Workers who overextend themselves feel
run down, overly tired, and discouraged. Incorporating a habit
of creating time to reflect on your life can help restore balance.
This chapter offers information and poses questions to encourage reflection on the causes of overwork in your life or in the
lives of those around you, and what can be done to re-establish
life balance.

Why do people overwork? Consider these four possibilities:
They work too much out of necessity, because their interests and
talents don't match the job, in response to outside pressure, or

because they believe that their job is the best option. They can't imagine doing anything else.

Out *of* Necessity

When someone must work two or three jobs to make ends meet, the conditions are set for overwork. Picture an older woman with little formal education who receives minimum wage for her labors. Under a supervisor's watchful eye, she works in a garment factory stitching pockets on a never-ending assembly line of partially made jeans. After that shift, she goes to a part-time job in the environmental services department of a local hospital. Then she returns home to a third, unpaid job—caring for her daughter's three children.

Many people may not have the same burdens as this woman but experience financial pressures that lead to overwork. In this case, how you manage the household budget, follow shopping impulses, and distinguish needs from wants determines your financial condition. A closer examination of your daily activities may reveal that you create the financial necessity leading to overwork. Could overwork be a result of choices rather than true necessity? It's an important distinction. Are we victims or perpetrators of overwork? The following exercise may help you answer that question. After you complete it, continue on to page 181.

Tip No. 16

to Help Ourselves

Look *at* Why You Work *the* Way You Do

If you're caught in the trap of overwork, turn to these journal pages and answer these questions:

- Do I feel run down, tired or over extended?

- Is my heart in my work?

- Is it really necessary to work as I do?

- What are the rewards of working as I do?

- What are the drawbacks of overwork?

- What is my heart's desire when it comes to work?

- Is it realistic to believe that I can make a living by doing what I enjoy?

THE BENEFIT TO YOU: This reflective exercise will help you identify whether you overwork and how your actions and choices perpetuate this condition. Reflection and awareness mark the beginning of the end of this unhealthy pattern. ✎

Case Study

THE IMPORTANCE OF HAVING A PERSONAL LIFE

Yesterday one of my directors asked me, "Are you dating someone?"

"Why do you ask?" I replied.

"You seem so happy. You don't seem as bothered by every little thing as you used to be."

Her question and comments shocked me. I didn't realize she had noticed that I had been upset by some of the things going on at work. I guess I was. What amazed me was that she was so observant and saw that my attitude at work has shifted quite a lot lately. I have started dating someone and I'm head over heels about him. I had no idea that my personal life could have such an influence on how I am at work.

YOUR INSIGHT: _____

_____

_____

_____

_____

LESSON: Reflection and self awareness are the beginning of changing behaviors and attitudes. Having a satisfying personal life influences our attitude in the workplace.

Job Mismatch

Some people work too hard because their interests and talents conflict with the type of job they have and what it requires. The greater the mismatch, the harder and longer it takes to complete assignments. Those who are well matched expend less energy. A physician looking back over his life wrote this in his journal:

"Residencies, great rotations. Enjoyed surgery the most. Hated psychiatry. Mind games. Obstetrics appealed. I remember thinking that I

shouldn't go in that direction. Women need women. I've never really enjoyed surgery even after all the success. The best thing that ever happened to me was joining my partners and making enough money to take a year off to write the novel. That's changed everything. I am more of a poet than surgeon. I knew that in my 20s but kept pushing the medical thing. I've got to look at why. Maybe I liked obstetrics because it was closer to beauty and mystery than fixing bones. I'm glad I jumped to writing. I feel more energy as a writer than I ever felt as a surgeon. I'm not as tired as I used to be. Poorer, yes. No turning back."

For workers who feel mismatched, options include keeping their job and focusing on the parts they enjoy, or looking for another job. They can also try to change themselves. Changing jobs is difficult and, due to fear or inertia, the least-chosen option, but it's also the most rewarding.

Everyone has a unique set of talents, abilities, interests, and preferences. A particular job may fit one person but not another. For some people, the physical environment is important; they need windows, light, and art on the walls as well as a place where they can connect with colleagues in meaningful ways. Others don't care much about the physical setting as long as they're doing something really enjoyable. A few prefer to work alone in a private office. In the following story, a nurse recalls an encounter with a man who seemed perfectly matched to his job:

"I've worked in this hospital for 22 years. Yesterday I met another employee who has been here even longer. Until yesterday, we had never met.

"I needed to go down to the facilities department to ask someone to raise the temperature in the hallways of the ICU. I had asked twice before to no avail. This time I thought I'd take matters into my own hands and go directly to the boiler room where I had never set foot. Since no one was answering my e-mails, I thought that if I met the manager face-to-face, I would be able to get the temperature changed.

"Talk about a surprise. I was overwhelmed by the size of the boiler room. The place was two stories high and almost half a football field long in a part of the hospital that was over 100 years old. The walls were a combination of brick and stone. It was windowless. The place reminded me of something you'd find in a Dickens novel. However, it did not resemble the kind of drab industrial surroundings he would write about. It was unimaginably clean and orderly. Pipes, large and small, were either parallel or at right angles to one another, each coded in a bright colors. It seemed as if someone had just dusted them. My thoughts turned to the condition of the refrigerator in our break room in the ICU. In contrast to this boiler room, I'd be embarrassed to have anyone other than a nurse open our refrigerator door.

"While the size, orderliness, and noise of the boiler room amazed me, my meeting with the employee was even more memorable. Before this meeting, I had never laid eyes on the guy. Would you believe he has worked in or around that room for 24 years? He told me the hospital hired him two weeks *after he left the military where he was trained as [a heating, ventilation, and air conditioning] specialist. He first worked various jobs within the facilities department. He said, 'I just went where I was needed.' Sixteen years ago, an administrator asked if he would consider becoming manager of the heating plant. 'Sure,' he told her. 'I've been here ever since. Over the years, everything has changed, but I love it. Wouldn't think of leaving. Somehow I just fit in down here. The nuns upstairs say it's my vocation. That's funny. I don't know why they say that. I've got a wife and three kids. I sure don't live like a nun.'*

"After a few minutes, I remembered why I came down to talk to him. 'Could you change the daytime temperature of the halls in the ICU?' I asked. 'No, I can't,' he responded. 'The control panel for that floor is across the city in one of our other hospitals. I'll call over and ask. It may take a moment or two.' That, too, was a shock. I had no idea that someone in one of our other hospitals controlled the temperature in a hallway of our hospital. I left the boiler room before he got an answer.

"As I left that bright, albeit dungeon-like place to catch the elevator to my floor, I thought to myself, 'That man is content to work in that out-of-the-way place for years on end. He even seemed peaceful. I'd say he was happy.' That got me thinking about myself. Do I fit my job the way he seems to fit his? I've also begun wondering about my nurses on the floor. Given the way nursing has changed over the years, I wondered if some of the frustration they feel is related to feeling mismatched to what is expected of them in today's hospital setting.

"I remember reading that Johnny Carson, more of a humorist than a philosopher, said that no one should 'continue in a job they don't enjoy. If you're happy in what you're doing, you'll like yourself and have inner peace. And if you have that, along with physical health, you will have had more success than you could possibly have imagined.'

"John Ruskin, the painter and philosopher, believed that 'in order that people may be happy in their work, these three things are needed: They must be fit for it, they must not do too much of it, and they must have a sense of success in it.'

"I'm going to talk about my experience of visiting the manager of the boiler room at our next staff meeting to see what nurses think."

Case Study

KNOWING WHEN IT'S TIME TO CHANGE JOBS

Last Friday during an executive team meeting, the vice president of nursing told a story about one of her managers being so angry at a staff nurse, "she wanted to kill her."

The vice president said she quipped to this manager, "That's a little strong. It wouldn't look good if we had to tell the board that you killed her. Do you really want to kill her?"

"Of course not," the manager replied. "I'll settle for giving her a good shake!"

The vice president said she remembered hearing a similar threat when she was a child: "It didn't seem to help me change my ways as a youngster. I doubt if it will work with adults."

When the manager was asked what made her so angry, she replied, "That's easy. The nurse is dead wood. She doesn't carry her weight and she always has a bad attitude."

Work should be, and usually is, enjoyable. When it isn't, something's wrong. The trouble may have to do with employees who are dissatisfied, with those who express their unhappiness at work, or with other issues. Often enough, we all carry unseen burdens that understandably influence our demeanor. Our troubles can explain but not excuse bringing a sour disposition to work.

Everyone needs to be engaged in work they enjoy. Otherwise, it's time to look for another job. This is even more critical for health care professionals because their work so deeply and meaningfully impacts the lives of those they are trained and committed to help.

YOUR INSIGHT: _____

_____

_____

_____

_____

LESSON: If you're no longer enjoying work, it's time to move on. No patient needs a sour caregiver.

Are you in the right job? The following exercise may help you answer that question. After you've finished it, continue reading on page 189.

Ask: Am I *in the* Right Job?

In this exercise, you will till the soil to awaken insight. Read and mull the following questions, then respond in these journal pages. To make this exercise valuable and effective, allow for a full expression of ideas and avoid yes or no answers. Freely write what comes to mind, and don't worry about clarity or even accuracy. Trust yourself—don't judge or second-guess yourself and let your thoughts flow effortlessly.

There will be time in the future to clarify, amend, or delete what you've written. Ready to start? Reflect and jot down your thoughts, feelings and reactions to the following questions:

- Does my job honestly interest me?

- Do I feel like I'm working in a half-hearted manner?

- Did I choose this job or did I fall into it?

- At work, are my interests and talents fully used?

- Am I in over my head without the competencies my job requires?

- Do I have vague, lingering feelings that I'm misplaced in my job?

- People with balanced lives tend to take time away from work when they're tired. Overworked people tend to push on. What do I do?

THE BENEFIT TO YOU: Denial keeps us stuck; awareness is the first step to reenergize your life. What a relief to know whether or not you're in the right job! And if you aren't, you'll gain insight and clarity into why you're feeling drained at work, and start the process of finding the right job for you! ✑

Case Study

MAKING A JOB CHANGE FOR THE RIGHT REASONS

Thoughts that a nurse shared at an off-campus workshop:

"For years I practiced as a nurse midwife at two well-known hospitals. I loved the work, I was good at it, and I found it particularly rewarding.

"Out of the blue, I received a call from a nurse-recruiter who wanted to know if I'd consider taking a job in a New York City hospital as the director of women's services. They were looking for someone with midwifery experience as well as experience in ICU and emergency department settings. My CV fit the bill.

"I really had never thought about leaving Denver, but I must honestly say that the call flattered me. So did the money. The salary range was almost double what I was receiving. Since my divorce, I've always worried about retirement. It didn't take long to figure out that the new job would solve that problem for good.

"The long and short of it is that I took the job. I lasted two years to the day. It was a mistake from the word "go." Catching babies is a whole different world from arranging schedules, dealing with labor issues, and resolving staff conflicts. The hospital's culture and even the city rubbed me the wrong way.

"I called my former employer and would you believe that the Denver hospital welcomed me back? Because I was away for two years, I had to accept a drop in salary. At this point, who cares? I'd rather work in my old hospital in Denver than in that New York City hospital for twice the money. Money is seductive."

YOUR INSIGHT:

_____

_____

_____

_____

_____

LESSON: Meaningful work is one thing; working to acquire wealth is another. Think twice before changing jobs to solve a problem that is completely unrelated to your work.

Pressure _from_ Others

Pressure from others—a spouse, the boss, a colleague—also causes people to overwork. A heightened sensitivity and concern about what others think adds to this pressure. Overworked individuals typically say they want to please that person or they're afraid that person will think poorly of or reject them if they don't meet his or her expectations. If this need to please others or fear of rejection is strong, it will likely lead to feeling and being overworked.

It might come as a surprise, but more often than not, the source of such thinking comes exclusively from within ourselves as the voice of an idealized internal self. When we hear the voice say, "I should be able to do this," or "I ought to be able to do that," it is the "perfect" person you have internalized and allowed to run your life as a tyrant. The late Karen Horney, a German psychoanalyst, had a wonderfully clear explanation of how this occurs. She wrote that everyone has a real self, or who we are, and an ideal self, or who we think we ought to be. Patients taught her that it's easy to get caught between the two. It's also easy to be tyrannized by the ideal self into thinking we should do something—a phenomenon Horney called the "tyranny of the shoulds."[1]

The next exercise is designed to help you better understand "shoulds." After you've completed it, turn to page 191 to learn more about overwork.

Tip No. 18
to Help Ourselves

Recognize Who Moves You *to* Work *as* You Do

Individuals who are well matched to their jobs tend to focus on teamwork and getting the job done. Those who are mismatched generally feel they must push themselves to get the job done.

Pretend that a trustworthy person asks you the questions below and a discussion ensues. Write down a few notes about the conversation as if you can remember all the details.

- Are you driven by fear? [Whether yes or no, provide details.]

- Are you searching for acceptance? If so, why?

- What would happen if you changed the way you work?

- If you did, who would you please?

- Who would you displease?

- At work, are you authentic—true to yourself, your values, your personality?

- If not, what would happen if you were?

THE BENEFIT TO YOU: You will become aware of how much pressure you feel from your idealized internal voice: You know, the one demanding that you be perfect. Identifying and understanding that voice is the first step toward pushing the mute button on it! ᴒ

Nothing Better *to* Do

Because their work is highly rewarding, successful and gifted individuals spend so much time in work-related activities that their lives become narrow, often without them even realizing it. They enjoy their work and are competent at everything. Accomplished nurses are on top of their game in caring for patients, working with colleagues, and perhaps managing staff. Accomplished teachers are admired by students and fellow faculty and like taking the time to creatively prepare for classes. Accomplished surgeons keep an open mind by following the latest research, attending conferences, and conferring with other medical professionals to improve their skills.

However, as a highly successful and talented person devotes more and more time to work or work-related activities, his life may narrow and work can become the only thing that genuinely interests him. A ballet in town, World Series fever, a new book with a fresh perspective on the Civil War—nothing else draws his attention away from that myopic focus on work. He may be glad that others find these activities intriguing, exciting, and stimulating, but he has no time or interest in pursuing anything outside of work. The result is an increasingly narrow life. French researchers refer to this phenomenon as *déformation*—the de-formation of one's personality.

Tip No. 19 will help you determine if you work too much. In Chapter 6, we'll look at creative ways for the overworked to restore a healthier work-life balance.

Case Study

A physician talking about his doctor friend:

"One of my best friends is a physician who for years has been a stickler for perfection as the chief of surgery and the director of the residency program. Before taking this appointment, he was in the armed forces for 20 years.

"'I'm a take-charge kind of guy' was his favorite saying when teaching the residents, 'and I want you to be the same.' 'Make a decision and act' was another of his maxims. Everyone referred to him as a doctor's doctor. He had one interest: surgery. I'd almost say the operating room was his life. His patients seemed to love him. Most nurses in the OR were tolerant of his demands but were not enamored of his personality.

"His wife is a nurse at another hospital. They came over to our home every couple of weeks for a light meal and conversation. Once, while we were doing dishes and he was not within earshot, his wife said to me, 'Medicine is the only thing that interests him. He's 52. I can't imagine our next 25 years together. We love each other, but we'll probably go our separate ways.'"Last year they divorced."

YOUR INSIGHT: _____

_____

_____

_____

_____

LESSON: Having very few interests outside of work indicates a problem, not a reason to admire and compliment someone.

Inventory Your Interests

Tip No. 19

to Help Ourselves

When people are overworked, their curiosity and interests diminish or even disappear. Things that used to thrill them—music, art, theatre, nature, travel—become distant memories or are forgotten. Although such individuals may think they know themselves well, it's time to question that belief. It's exciting to think that you are a mystery even to yourself. There is much to explore and learn.

Use the questions below to discover if you overwork:

- Have I heard others say that I work too much? Who said it? When? Why?

- Did I used to have interests or hobbies that I've replaced with work? What were they?

- What are my actual interests based on the time I spend pursuing them?

- Do I spend time away from work resting up before I return?

THE BENEFIT TO YOU: Determining if you've let go of past interests and hobbies is the key to unlocking your passions that have been restrained by overwork. Awareness is your *Get Out of Jail Free* card. Use it! ᴥ

A Reflection

This week, a wonderful friend and colleague lost her job as the administrator of a thriving stand-alone clinic. I don't know why her employment was ended, but I do know that the Board was pleased with her service, generosity, and commitment. "She was totally dedicated. It's just time for her to move on. We need new blood."

I also know she feels betrayed. "How could they have done this to me? My heart and soul were invested in that place. You can't imagine the hours I put in. I worked myself to the bone. If I had gotten sick working the way I was, I doubt if they would've noticed. All those hours put in and this is what I get for it! It's not fair."

Though she is not yet able to recognize the way in which the Board appreciated her selflessness, there will come a time when she will. For now, all she feels is confusion, anger and resentment. She has stumbled into the trap of thinking—as many of us do—that if she worked really hard, even to the point of overextending herself, that others would notice and reward her accordingly. "How could they do this to me? Don't they know how hard I've worked? They owe me big time. Where is their loyalty?"

Organizations are larger than any of us. They need new blood, new ways of thinking, and leadership styles. That is all for the better. It is also true that we, as individuals, need to be appreciated, acknowledged and supported. We need the stability that loyalty provides.

A problem is born when we link our personal well being a little too closely to that of the organization. Perhaps that is why my friend feels as she does. Conversely, it is also a problem when an organization's identity is linked with a specific individual. Who has not seen organizations falter when their leaders think of the organization as their own?

In many ways, employment is a teacher of sorts. Thoreau wrote that he went into the woods to see what he could learn, and not wait until he came to die to discover that he had not lived.

Those of us who work within the caring professions may not need to go into the woods to learn about our work patterns and situation. Our work becomes our teacher. The ups and downs of our work lives—its satisfactions and disappointments—teach us about our selves and how to work without losing perspective. With time, my friend will be the better for having experienced losing her job just as all of us ultimately benefit from having suffered through, and learned from, our seeming failures. I suspect she will be learning about her motivation as well as her expectations regarding employment.

What have you learned about yourself? Here's what the Little Prince has to say about life: "Living is being born slowly. It would be a little too easy if we could borrow ready-made souls." ❤

Notes

Notes ～

Notes ❧

Notes ⤳

Notes

6

From Overwork *to a* Healthier Work-Life Balance

"A vigorous five-mile walk will do more good for
an unhappy but otherwise healthy adult than all of
the medicine and psychology in the world."

PAUL DUDLEY WHITE, MD,

FATHER OF AMERICAN CARDIOLOGY

When it seems like overwork has caused us to lose the balance between our work life and personal life, and we feel driven, coerced, or spiritless, living reflectively helps restore balance. Overworked individuals blindly react to inner messages or outside influences and pressures—and sometimes both. These inner messages drive them mercilessly. Perhaps these are voices carried over from early childhood. Or maybe they are propelled by an urgent need to feel perfect and in control. Coercion, in contrast, comes from the outside—from bosses, co-workers, spouses, parents, children, financial stress, or other social and cultural sources. People who abdicate or surrender their power to these internal and external forces, whose lives are shaped by reactions to situations rather than by conscious choice, become passive and resentful victims. They forfeit responsibility for their lives and blame forces they believe are beyond their control.

The Value *of* Reflection

Adding a few moments of reflection to our daily lives is an immediate antidote to the feelings of powerlessness and resentment that arise from living reactively. It puts distance between us and those internal and external forces, if only for a moment, and gives us an opportunity to make conscious choices about the direction of our lives. Given the pace of contemporary life, the problem is finding time and space for reflection. That's especially challenging for people who are battling work fixation, addiction, or exhaustion—all of which are distorted, unhealthy behaviors that fill any possible space for reflection.

Case Study

CHOOSING WHAT TO LEAVE UNDONE

A pharmacy manager talking to her staff:

"Have you ever started the day with having to get five things done but you only have time for three of them? You know two are going to be left undone when you leave work. I've had that experience more than once.

"I've discovered a couple of things about that situation. One is that the world does not collapse when an important task is left unfinished at the end of the day. I have also learned that the most important decision we can make is to decide what not to do. That sounds easy. It isn't. However, if you don't do it, you will drive yourself mad. Besides, no one has time to do all they want to do. Show me people who are able to finish everything on their plates and I will show you people who have either died or are kidding themselves."

YOUR INSIGHT:

_____

_____

_____

_____

LESSON: When you're at work, sit down and prioritize what has to get done and own up to what you can't do. When you're at home, think of yourself as unfinished, as a work in progress with shortcomings or issues that need to be resolved. Self-reflection is the beginning. Patience is the challenge. Until you look at yourself and commit to owning your imperfections, you may never slow down.

The first task in living reflectively is to get overwork under control, which the four suggestions and related exercises in Tip No. 20 will help you accomplish. Think of overwork as an outer layer to be peeled away before you can confront the problems underneath that lead to work fixation, addiction, or exhaustion. Fortunately, overworked people tend to be dutiful and persistent, traits that will help them escape distorted, unhealthy work behaviors. After you review Tip No. 20, turn to page 211.

Tip No. 20

to Help Ourselves

Create *an* Anti-Overwork Clock *and* Calendar

This suggestion is only for those who know they consistently overwork—that is, spend more time at work than appropriate, given their particular physical, mental, and spiritual energies—and want to change. Creating a 24-hour clock is a good first step.

Draw the clock (see figure) as you would a 12-hour clock. Then, recall a typical day and estimate as accurately as possible how many hours you devoted to each activity—working, sleeping, eating, watching television, working out, reading, surfing the Internet, traveling, playing, etc. You may want to shade each activity-related segment of hours with a different color. Be honest. You're the only one who will see the clock. If you don't like it, you can draw another clock portraying another day.

This completed clock reflects what you value. To gain insight into those values, study the clock and, in these journaling pages, reflect on what you see:

• Do you spend too many or too few hours at work?

• Do your weekends resemble weekdays?

• Do you maintain your health in body, mind and spirit by

giving yourself sufficient time for sleep, relaxation, quiet activities, physical exercise, and eating?

- Are you able to do some of these activities without the project-like stance you assume at work?

For perspective on activities that may be valued but forgotten, refer to Thomas Moore's description of a "soulful" life on page 39.

Now, it's time to take a longer look at how you use your time. Look ahead and prepare a rigidly scheduled 12-month calendar. You don't have to wait for January 1; your year can start today. It's important to see the entire year laid out—a schedule of activities you want to include in your life. Don't worry about what's practical. Pretend you live in an ideal world. For instance, you might pencil in exercise three days a week or time for education, professional training, or spiritual refreshment. Now's the time to schedule that extended vacation you haven't had in years.

Once you've finished the calendar, make three commitments to yourself:

COMMITMENT 1: Show it to two significant persons, preferably a loved one and an authority figure at work.

COMMITMENT 2: Promise to adhere to the schedule as the year unfolds. A rigid schedule can actually free a person who is unable to control the demands of work because it allocates unstructured time and "permission" to use that time to meet personal needs.

COMMITMENT 3: If it's necessary to change your schedule because something unexpected comes up, you must reschedule any missed activities. Don't revert to the past pattern of overlooking what you know is good for your health.

THE BENEFIT TO YOU: This exercise is your passport out of the Land of Overwork! It is a concrete mapping out of a new life that will support a healthier, happier, more balanced way to live. Why wait? The time is now! ❧

The reason it's important to show this completed calendar to a loved one and an authority figure at work, perhaps an administrator, will become evident as the year unfolds. Suppose the calendar includes going away for a few days away in February to a retreat-like setting, far from your snow-covered part of the country. Warm, dry air in the Southwest is exactly what you'll need to refresh your spirits. You've scheduled a workshop in Santa Fe, New Mexico, and the administrator approves. However, as luck would have it, the hospital subsequently schedules a key meeting and expects you to attend. In the past, you would have dropped everything to be there. This time, you go to your administrator, calendar in hand, and tell her about your dilemma: "This is what I planned. It's what I need. I'd like to keep to that plan unless it's absolutely necessary for me to stay for the meeting."

The administrator's response? I suspect it will be something like: "Go! I'd much rather you take care of yourself and return refreshed and engaged. We don't need one more dutiful person moping around here working half-heartedly. Enjoy the trip. I hear that there are slots in the Las Vegas airport. Here's an extra $50. Have fun." Sound unreal? It's not. This near-verbatim quote is from an administrator I worked with at a large hospital in the Northeast.

On the other hand, suppose she says, "No, we really need you here. I'd prefer you didn't go." If this happens, the third commitment you made to yourself comes into play: Reschedule the activity for another time during the same year. It has to be the same year because dutiful, overworked individuals tend to selflessly extend themselves and thus remain caught in the trap of overwork. "I'll do it next year" is the same as saying, "I'll keep living as I always have."

Here's how a man attending a weekend retreat reacted when I suggested that strategy:

"What you're suggesting is unreasonable. Who lives that way? Who can schedule life that way? Maybe your local neurotic does. I don't. There are meetings to attend and things to do that can never be foreseen. How can I tell when my kids are going to get sick? Who can predict what I have to do at the office? I don't live by that kind of planning."

Workers who need a calendar will be cheating themselves if they don't take advantage of this useful tool as it helps people take charge of their lives and set a tone of balanced priorities. Otherwise, they will continue to feel like others are living their lives because, in fact, they are. It's only natural that overworked individuals' stress and resentment grow along with anger toward others whose requests, demands, and needs structure the way they live. The alternative? Create a solution where overworked individuals take back control of their lives.

You may be thinking, "This all sounds too self-centered. We need to forget about ourselves and get down to work. There's too much self-pity, too much introspection." This attitude keeps people stuck in unhealthy patterns of working and living. They are more likely to defend against their condition by staying in denial, blaming others, and maintaining the status quo. "We may be miserable," they say, "but it's our very own misery! We know it, we're comfortable with it, and we can't do anything about it." As a result, they downplay their inner needs, including the need for quiet reflection, which in turn continues to exact a cost on their physical, mental, and spiritual health.

John Bohn, a business consultant, reminds high-functioning executives to take care of their bodies. "It's the only place you have to live!" he tells them. That's sound advice for us all.

Scheduling activities a year ahead is a way to insert space into our days and thereby avoid overwork. To the degree we successfully adhere to the schedule and own our activities, we can create opportunities for reflection, which slows the frenetic pace of daily life.

Case Study

TAKING REFLECTIVE TIME MAKES PEOPLE MORE EFFECTIVE AT WORK

A journal entry of a manager in accounts payable:

"The most important thing for me to do today is to complete four performance reviews due on Friday. They've been on my desk for three weeks. One reason I procrastinate is that I hate doing them.

"The funny thing is that I know how to help myself. All I need to do is go to an out-of-the-way corner of the cafeteria for 10 or 15 minutes and read something inspirational. That settles me. After taking that small amount of time for myself, it's relatively easy to do things I need to do but don't like doing. The problem is that I forget to take that quiet time apart from the demands of my daily work."

YOUR INSIGHT: _____

_____

_____

_____

LESSON: It's so easy to forget that we work better and more effectively when we find protected time to be alone.

The next exercise involves carving out time for such reflection. After you've reviewed it, turn to page 216 to learn more about "doing nothing."

ୈ୭ଡ଼ୟ

Tip No. 21

to Help Ourselves

ୈୱ୭ଡ଼ୟ

Schedule 15 Minutes Each Day *to* Do Nothing

Try to take 15 minutes for reflection early in the morning or at the beginning of your day, before you're swept up by the routines and external demands of the day. Early morning is an ideal time because, despite a surface grogginess, people usually wake up in a calm, trance-like condition that makes them more open to unexpected revelations and insights. See Tip No. 23 on page 227 for some ideas on how to create a reflective space at home. If it's more realistic to take these 15 minutes at work, the hospital chapel, outside gardens, labyrinth or other meditative space in your hospital will work. A simple meditative walk around the block will suffice if that's all that's available at the moment.

During these 15 minutes, you might daydream or muse about the way you live. Your thoughts may turn to other people in your life or to the long workday ahead. This time is unique in that you don't get up and start doing things. You simply reflect.

THE BENEFIT TO YOU: This simple (but not always easy) act of setting aside time for reflection could be the most productive, beneficial 15 minutes you spend all day. The benefit? Peace of mind, clarity, a full reservoir of peace that you can draw on all day, and a heightened sense of awareness and presence. All from 15 minutes of alone time. Daily. ᴄ~

At first glance, taking 15 minutes a day to do nothing may seem easy enough. But what does that really mean? We're always doing something, even if it's just sitting still, watching TV, surfing the Internet, filing our nails, folding laundry, rifling through the mail, or some other mundane task. So another way of thinking of this is that we need to create time for quiet.

It's almost impossible for the overworked person to take time for reflection, particularly early in the day. She might say, "Why sit and do nothing? Anyone can do that. I've got things to do. The sooner I get things done, the better I'll feel. What I need is more time in the day. I don't need to waste time doing nothing." The fact is, many people—especially those who are overworked, work addicted, or work fixated—can't sit still, or aren't aware of the benefit of "doing nothing." However, as the following conversations illustrate, one can benefit from this simple act just by trusting the process and doing it:

"I heard you've been trying to do nothing for 15 minutes each morning. How's it going?"

"No problem at all. Seems useless, but I'm doing this for the hell of it."

• • •

"Are you still taking some quiet time during the day? How's it going?"

"I'm still doing it most of the time, maybe four days a week. Nothing is happening!"

"What did you do this morning?"

"Nothing, I just sat there. I heard my favorite song on the radio, which I really enjoyed."

• • •

"Are you still doing that 15 minutes of nothing?"

"Most of the time."

"Have you had any insights?"

"No, but this morning I remembered that I thought for awhile about giving up cigarettes. The one I was smoking left a lousy taste in my mouth and I thought, 'I may as well try to stop smoking as long as I'm on this kick of trying to live a more balanced life.'"

• • •

"You won't believe it, but you know what I realized this morning? For the past four weeks, I've clipped my nails every morning in the first few minutes of my 'doing nothing' time."

It is difficult for many of us to sit and do nothing for fifteen minutes. Try it for a few days to experience how difficult it is. The work-driven side of our personality may overlook the importance of carving out quiet time and the benefits it yields and yet the benefits are enormous. Quiet time helps us become conscious of the forgotten life teeming within: The richness of our ideas and creativity; the novel ways we unconsciously solve problems; and the random thoughts about people whom we hold dear. All of these thoughts often get shoved aside by immediate, urgent demands along with the pleasurable activities we've set aside—maybe hiking in the woods, playing with pets, listening to classical music, or having tea with old friends.

Accessing such thoughts and sentiments requires a body at rest in peaceful surroundings. Reaching for a book, lighting a cigarette, turning on the radio, checking e-mail or phone messages, sipping coffee, clipping our nails, or other seemingly innocent acts can easily distract us from that inward life. One of the gifts of doing nothing, aside from its value in perhaps helping us solve a problem, see a situation in a whole new way, or recall past interests, is the few minutes we devote exclusively to ourselves.

Doing nothing doesn't mean emptying the mind of all thoughts. It's much easier than that. Rather, uninterrupted moments are simply about spending time with our selves, without a particular project in mind. As Chapter 3 explained, going about daily life with a project in mind is what makes any activity work. Uninterrupted moments are an attempt to move apart from near constant work.

Case Study

THE BENEFITS OF "DOING NOTHING"

The effort to set aside time to do nothing may seem pointless, however, when undertaken systematically, there are surprisingly good reasons to persevere and cultivate this activity into a lifelong habit. In addition to the benefits mentioned in this chapter, taking time to "do nothing" seems to help people work more efficiently and creatively. Here's how two highly successful men, both of them teachers (one is also a writer), described their experiences of doing nothing each day:

TEACHER: *"I love those 15 minutes. I wouldn't stop them for anything. When I sit there, I think of all the things that I have to do during the day and then jot them down. Then I arrange them in order of importance and tack them up on the refrigerator door. What a great help it is. I'm more realistic about what I can do during the day, and at night I have a sense of accomplishment."*

TEACHER/WRITER: *"The reason I like to take time for reflection before I go to sleep at night is that my imagination is more stimulated in the morning. That helps me with my poetry. I write down the images that come up at the time. During the day, I work them out. I'm publishing more these days and I feel more alive."*

YOUR INSIGHT:

_____

_____

_____

_____

_____

LESSON: Sometimes it's important to try something new even if you're skeptical about whether it will work. By trying to "do nothing" for 15 minutes a day, you could reap huge rewards, and you don't need to know what they'll be or when they will happen. It might even be more effective if you don't. Trust the process.

Overworked people may be attracted to the discipline of scheduling time for early morning reflection because, among other rewards, it enables them to organize their day, formulate to-do lists, and set their sights on another highly productive day. And therein lies a danger. Discovering how quiet time can improve productivity simply feeds into their overwork behavior. It doesn't help them understand why they overwork. With practice, they'll see that quiet time is far more beneficial if they don't use it to make lists or organize the day.

Overwork leads us to lose track of our life direction—our feelings, hopes and aspirations. Used wisely, 15 minutes of quiet reflection helps us rediscover our lives. Another way to think of reflection is as a contemplative space where we rest with the world rather than create it.

Do you still think doing nothing is unrealistic? If so, that's understandable. It may require a giant leap of faith. After all, in our fast-paced world, people in their prime don't place much value on doing nothing. As one busy nurse and mom said, "It may be OK for children. It is certainly understandable that older people may welcome it. It just seems useless to me. I'll wait for that kind of thing for when I'm on the beach next summer." Although breaking the hold of overwork isn't easy, it's the doorway to a work and personal life that's more meaningful, joyful, and enriching. Quiet reflection frees us from the stranglehold of overwork and leads us on our journey as evolving spiritual beings.

Athletes know how difficult it is to alter habits. For example, younger tennis pros who haven't reached their peak resist learning new moves, like a better way to serve or volley. Many mediocre tennis players, according to coaches, believe that all they have to do is try harder. Unfortunately, while such an attitude reflects self-confidence, it's wrong. Players who can let go of their old serve and accept the coach's unfamiliar technique way may struggle for a time, but often, their game ultimately improves.

Jettisoning a pattern of overwork is immensely more difficult than learning a new tennis serve, yet the dynamics are similar. Escaping overwork involves cultivating a more reflective inner life that will lead us to change how we use time. The reward? An enriched life.

The Power *of* Words

An aggressive man who wants to become more gentle will begin to achieve this goal when he voices tender sentiments. A diffident woman who recognizes her insecurity will become more confident as she learns to voice her thoughts and feelings. These simple examples illustrate the sacredness and the power of words and the role they play in creating the world. Words are prophetic in that they announce what will be, which is why one of the most important ways to escape the hold of overwork is to be attentive to the words we use when speaking with each other. Consider this brief exchange between two people who meet in a hallway at work:

"Are you busy?"

"Yes. You wouldn't believe how busy I am. I have to…"

The person who affirms how busy she is does what most of us do. Using words, she gives an already fast-turning wheel— her life—a slap to keep it moving. She also affirms her value to herself and others. In many work settings, people are praised and admired when they have a lot to do, which gives them a sense of self-importance.

What would happen if this woman, even though she's extremely busy, changed her accustomed pattern of speaking? For example:

"Are you busy?"

"No, I'm not too busy."

At first, her response may sound like a lie. Why tell someone you aren't pressured when you are? The fact is, almost everyone is busy, particularly those who overwork. We all have unfinished projects. However, much of the anxiety we feel is of our own making, and saying, "No, I'm not too busy" breaks that cycle. The effect is immediate. Once a person says she isn't too busy, she will find it difficult to continue speaking about her frenetic pace.

Consider this scenario:

"Are you busy?"

"No."

"Good. Could you help me?"

"No, not right now."

"But I thought you said you're not busy."

"I'm not. I can help if you really need me now, but I'll have to limit the amount of time I give you."

Is this response selfish? It largely depends on the speaker's attitude and tone of voice. Her answer is an effort to live honestly. There are always people who need help. The question is, are we the only ones who can help at that moment?

Another often-used coping strategy is denial, where the only way to relax is to deny seeing what must be done. Denial and avoidance are not effective ways to confront the pressure of overwork. In this example, the key is finding an effective and authentic way to help that supports our commitment to living a balanced, healthy life.

Even though someone may feel uncomfortable saying she won't help the other person right now unless it's really necessary, the long-term effect of speaking this truth is liberating. Words and phrases create a universe both spoken and unspoken. If I can relax when others are working ("I'll have to limit the amount of time I give you"), it becomes acceptable for others to relax when I am working. This is how work (and home) environments change.

Picture the employee who, sitting for a few minutes on a well-deserved break, suddenly jumps up when the boss walks in. The worker needn't say a word. The unspoken rule in this case is, "It's not OK to relax when the boss is around."

The challenge and opportunity is nurturing a work climate of honesty and trust where teams discuss what it means to honor the need for rest even when work needs to be done. In a climate where work and self care are in harmony, the person taking a break models respect for himself as well as co-workers. There's an understanding that taking a break is valued. There's also an understanding that when someone genuinely needs help, the person at rest will respond.

Without such honesty, busyness easily slips into compulsive activity and resentment builds because people feel forced to take on projects or complete tasks they don't want to do. Passive aggressive behavior may appear: Workers punish themselves or the person who assigned the project or task. Their words—or silence and inability to speak up—create a hostile atmosphere.

When we can honestly use affirming words, we create a place where we all want to work. These words may simply acknowledge that someone else is living as we'd like to live. "Glad to see you relaxing" is a great start. Such words not only help others, but also create an environment in which we too can relax when the need arises.

It's often difficult to affirm others when we see them relaxing because we are still a little uncomfortable with the "being" versus the "doing" side of life. Nevertheless, people who pay attention to their words discover the rewards of slowing down and find work-life balance in a relatively short time.

Along with quiet reflection, the following two tips will help you restore that balance.

Watch Your Speech

Tip No. 22

to Help Ourselves

Change your accustomed pattern of speaking. Change begins with awareness, and reflective writing can prompt awareness. In these journaling pages, jot down your thoughts on the following:

- Recall a particularly significant conversation. Write about what made it so meaningful. How did you feel during that conversation? To help you in future conversations, record the words that you use in everyday life. Knowing which words support meaningful conversation will encourage their use in the future.

- Think of a time when you regretted what you said. Some times our regret is linked to the words we use. However, it's the feelings behind the words that get us into trouble. How do we express anger or resentment without hurting another person? Can we express these feelings (and others) honestly and directly without shaming or hurting another? What words would you use to voice an insight or make a request with empathy rather than one tinged with anger or resentment?

THE BENEFIT TO YOU: Becoming aware that words shape your life is a huge step toward creating a new personal world order. Take back control of your life by honestly saying "yes" and "no." It starts with a commitment to living a healthy life and to creating and participating in a work (and home) environment built on trust, honesty, and the value of self care. It's liberating to honestly express our needs and equally freeing to those around us who then feel they can do the same. ～

Tip No. 23
to Help Ourselves

Create Space Where You Can Be Someone Other *than a* Worker

When the economy is rosy and jobs are secure, a buzz in the air leads us to buy whatever we want. When the economy falters and jobs are lost, we wisely scale back.

The same is not true when we're driven to overwork or we feel overwhelmed by the never-ending onslaught of competing demands. In these situations, many conscientious people simply work harder to get on top of their responsibilities, which compounds rather than relieves stress.

One of the most effective solutions for overwork is to simplify your life. That creates mental space. Artists, mystics, and naturalists know how to do this; they just turn their backs on the way most other people live and retreat to a place where they can pursue their interests. Think of Gandhi, Albert Schweitzer, Mother Theresa, Nelson Mandela, Martin Luther

King Jr., and the thousands of less famous professionals, artists, technicians, and researchers far from public view who limit life's choices so that they can follow their hearts' desires. Gandhi ended his law practice to follow his calling of becoming a leader. Schweitzer, a man with remarkable talent in music, philosophy, medicine, and theology, limited his life to caring for the medical needs of the under-served. Nelson Mandela set aside all of his personal needs, including his health and freedom, in order to lead his country. The compiled writings of Martin Luther King, Jr. reflect a single mindedness that is sobering and compelling. All of these leaders demonstrate life choices involving personal sacrifice; where to take one road means we do not take another.

The biographies of Gandhi, Albert Schweitzer, Mother Theresa, Nelson Mandela, and Martin Luther King Jr. also reveal how they scaled back their living quarters and created a space where they found the strength to follow their hearts' desire. These leaders and famous people serve as examples of how we can shape our lives—physically, emotionally and spiritually. We don't have to become a Mother Theresa to live a reflective life, but we can be inspired by her example to create a space and adopt elements of reflective living that will bring a new measure of peace and meaning into our lives.

In practice, living in a non-work way also means creating physical space for reflection only. The insights experienced there will ultimately help you work more effectively. The space could be a small room, an open porch, a garage, or something as small as the corner of an attic. In any case, it must enliven you, enable rest, focus your attention, and make you feel at home with yourself. Be sure to decorate this space with objects of personal value—those that hold significant memories and express your dreams. Remove objects that aren't inspirational. Once you've created this space, you will have a perfect spot for practicing Tip No. 21: Spending 15 minutes doing nothing.

THE BENEFIT TO YOU: Creating a physical, emotional and spiritual space for yourself is a strong signal you send to yourself and others that you are committed to living simply, reflectively and authentically.

A Reflection

TAKING BREAKS

Starbucks was packed. The line was out the door and there were only a few unoccupied easy chairs. It seems as if most were in a hurry to get out the door and off to work. There was one barista and three employees handling the crowd.

In the midst of all the activity, one of the employees left from behind the counter and came over to sit in one of the unoccupied soft chairs directly opposite me. She curled up, took out her phone, and began to check for whatever she was checking. Evidently it was time for her break.

While I was reading the paper, her presence interested me. I turned to see if there was still a long line. There was. I checked to see if another employee took this employee's place behind the counter. None had.

When our eyes caught one another's, I mumbled, "Wow, this place is busy." She merely smiled.

"Is it easy to take a break when there are so many in line?" I asked.

"Sure. We have to. It's policy."

"How do your buddies like it if you are here sitting and they are so busy behind the counter?"

"I don't know. I don't think we've ever talked about that. I know that I'm sorta glad when they take a break even if it's busy. We all need it."

That was the end of our conversation. However, I have thought about the interchange all day. Most of us know what it feels like not to take a break because there is too much to do. I know some employees who don't even take lunch. Seeing the ease with which the Starbuck's employee took her break, I wonder why those of us who work in hospitals, medical offices or nursing homes often do not take any breaks, sometimes not even for lunch.

Is this like comparing apples to oranges? Working with vulnerable patients in a health care setting is surely different from selling coffee at a Starbucks. I can imagine someone saying, "I wouldn't have any difficulty walking away from someone who wants their morning coffee either. Somebody will take care of them sooner or later. Taking care of patients is a whole other thing." True. However, no one is talking about walking away when patients are in need. Given that situation, all of us would stay until the patient's needs were met.

I once heard a CFO say that money drives the practice of working through breaks. "People can bill for the time if they work through their lunchtime or breaks. That amounts to significant dollars over time." Perhaps he is correct but I don't think so. After more than twenty-five years in health care, I haven't heard more than three or four employees say that they work through breaks for the money. The rest must be working through breaks for something else.

I suspect that the "something else" is more often than not the unspoken belief among team members that to be busy is good but to relax when there is work to be done is bad. As a result, breaks are not taken. It takes a gutsy person working within a health care setting to be seen relaxing when others are busy and in need of help. Is that person courageous or shamelessly selfish? That is a helpful question to ask during team meetings.

"People fail to get along because they fear each other; they fear each other because they don't know each other; they don't know each other because they have not communicated with each other."
Martin Luther King, Jr. ♥

Notes

Notes ⤳

Notes

Notes ✍

7

Two Rewards: Presence *and* Following Your Heart

"Our mind's desire is to know, to
understand; but our heart's desire is
intimacy, to be known, to be understood."

JOHN S. DUNNE, THE REASONS OF THE HEART

Taming work fixation, work addiction, or work exhaustion that leads to overwork is difficult. But success yields two huge rewards: an ability to live in the present moment and to hear and follow your heart's desires. Both bring a sense of peace.

Reward *No.* 1: Presence

Those of us who are work fixated, work addicted, or work exhausted have forgotten a core part of our inner selves. A telltale sign that we are in the grip of one or more of these distorted, unhealthy work behaviors is when others describe us as "preoccupied," "driven," "not all there," "absent-minded," "obsessed," or "distracted." Their perception is a kind of mirror reflecting something about ourselves that we might have otherwise denied or avoided. Their feedback is also a gift because it can spur us to take action.

If our nemesis is work fixation, others' description of us as "preoccupied" suggests that we're more interested in shaping the world to our purpose than appreciating the world as it is—with feelings of admiration, acceptance, and love. We experience what it means to be present once we can approach life without feeling the need to change everything and everyone in our path.

If our downfall is work addiction, we're at the mercy of inner forces driving us to the point that we can't stop our self-sabotaging, self-destructive behaviors. Once we harness those frenzied forces our pace slows almost magically, and we find a way to live in the here and now.

Case Study

RESENTMENT AND FEAR CAN PREVENT LIVING TODAY

An administrator's journal entry:

"After more than 30 years as a nurse, I've learned that many people—staff and patients alike—tend to have a difficult time living in the present moment. They are either filled with resentment from past hurts or afraid of what the future holds. Those two feelings, resentment and fear, rob us of energy and can get us into trouble. I know they had a role to play in my life.

"If I get stuck in past hurts, I can't get anything done. Instead of taking responsibility for myself, I blame others for what I don't like.

"If I'm afraid of the future, I can't work well because I'm preoccupied with what others will think, what they will say, or how I may fail.

"Both resentment and fear are self-defeating."

YOUR INSIGHT: _____

_____

_____

_____

_____

LESSON: If you're stuck in the past and if living with memories hurts, it's time for some soul searching. What resentments are you holding onto? When fear of a potential future event prevents you from taking action and living today, ask yourself, "What is it about the future that I fear?"

Colleagues, friends, and loved ones will notice the change but may not know the secret behind our newly-found peace: An escape from inner forces that drove us for years.

If our downfall is work exhaustion, others sense that our hearts are no longer invested in what we do. But when we start following our calling and begin living a more meaningful life, we slowly rediscover energy and purpose. Our inward lives become aligned with the liveliness of the workaday world and work energizes us again. We're not only present but also at home with ourselves—a gift we won't take for granted or lightly squander. Money, prestige, power, or any number of other attractions will have lost their allure now that we've experienced the profound and lasting value of living and working authentically. Being present becomes part of our everyday routine, as illustrated in this entry from the journal of James Lynch, a psychologist, researcher, and author:

On the evening of a late winter's day…a 75-year-old man lay in bed in an intensive care unit with his wife standing quietly beside him, gently stroking his hand while the flash of each heartbeat on the nurses' central monitoring station traced out the fact that he had had a severe heart attack earlier that morning. His electrocardiogram was markedly abnormal; runs of arrhythmic heartbeats caused the warning red light to flash brightly but ominously on the monitor, while intravenous needles dropped fluid into both his arms in a frantic effort to stave off the inevitable. For several hours before his life ended my father knew he was going to die, and he had only one simple request—that his wife of almost 48 years, my mother, stay by his side.

The pain from a heart that sorely ached from lack of oxygen made it difficult for him to speak, but between them words were not necessary. She gently stroked his hand for hours as his body temperature slowly dropped, until late in the evening he died peacefully, ending a lifetime of exquisite dialogue. The grief etched in my mother's face was the price of a commitment that knew no limits.

The next time I entered a hospital room, I was back at work at our university medical school. The very first patient I saw was my coronary nursing research assistant, who was sitting up in bed, tenderly holding her one-day-old son, her first child. She, too, was gently stroking a human being on the arm; he, too, could not speak, and between them words were equally unnecessary. The joy, pride, and peace that caused her to sparkle marked the beginning of a life of dialogue that also would know no limits.

Within a brief period I had come full circle, first witnessing the death of a person loved deeply, then witnessing life renewed. Common to both was human love, and in both cases its expression did not need spoken words. The essence of both of these encounters was dialogue, nonverbal dialogue—communication between those who are loved and in love.[1]

Would you want this man as your caregiver? He seems to be aware of himself and what's going on around him, sensitive to others, and able to respond to people in caring ways. I'd wager that no matter how many hours he works each week, he doesn't worry about finding balance in his life. Nor does he feel over-worked. He's wholly present in all of his activities, whatever they might be. If he has children, I suspect they love his playfulness. I'd be shocked if he doesn't have time to read, be with his wife, or work out at the gym.

Many busy people have found a way to live wholly present in body, mind, and spirit. How did they escape the hold of work addiction, fixation, or exhaustion?

One way is through protected time alone. This isn't a new concept. Just as you've found time to be present by writing in this journal, the second-century Roman Emperor Marcus Aurelius found it by writing in his journal, ultimately titled *Meditations*. Here's how Joseph Badaracco, a business professor at Harvard, described the emperor's work life and reflections:

Marcus knew full well the areas and responsibilities of practical life. He ruled a vast, diverse, unruly empire that spanned much of Europe, North Africa, and the Middle East. Marcus was…the chief priest of the Roman religion, and the highest judge in the Roman courts…. How did Marcus Aurelius combine the life of action with the spirit of reflection? How did he take the long view of the urgent tasks of the present moment? The answers lie in his personal journal. During the last years of his life, Marcus kept an informal record of his reflections, observations, and self-criticisms. He wrote for himself, not for the eyes of others. He wanted to understand who he was and how he should work and live. Marcus called the journal "To Himself," and only centuries later did it come to be called Meditations.[2]

What did Aurelius suggest we do to escape frenetic activity and loss of spirit?

The first lesson Marcus Aurelius might suggest for managers has nothing to do with work. In fact, its focus is on "not" working. Marcus's advice would be to work hard to create moments of serenity. Again and again, throughout Meditations, Marcus reminds himself to slow down and step back, to withdraw and reflect. He writes, "Are you distracted by outward cares? Then allow yourself a space of quiet, wherein you can add to your knowledge of the Good and learn to curb your restlessness." He tells himself, "Nowhere can a man find a quieter or more untroubled retreat than in his own soul." And again, "Avail yourself often, then, of this retirement, and so continually renew yourself."

This talk of retirement and retreat may sound otherworldly and monkish. It may suggest someone without the stomach for the hard work of trying to make a practical difference in the world. But there is no indication that Marcus ever shirked the duties and cares of his position. He ruled until his death—and may actually have hastened it—because he refused, to the very end, to lay down any of the duties and burdens of his office....

Were Marcus Aurelius alive today, he might well ask managers whether they have, somewhere in their lives, a counterpart to his tent, with its candle and plain table. He would be inquiring (discreetly and quietly—for he was, by all accounts, a gentle soul) not about a physical location, but about a mental retreat where they could reflect and renew themselves. Marcus might well be astonished and concerned at how infrequently the men and women who shoulder so many of the world's responsibilities remove themselves from other people, agendas, deadlines, telephones, and computers, and simply sit for a while and examine themselves, their lives, their thoughts and feelings.[3]

This advice from so long ago is still relevant today. Has writing in these journaling pages made you feel increasingly present? Read about the second reward on page 249.

Tip No.24
to Help Ourselves

Describe *the* Experience *of* Being Present

This tip builds on Tip No. 10, *Take Contemplative Walks.* Start by taking a contemplative walk, and then write reflectively in these journal pages. Remember, such a stroll is nothing more than an activity without purpose; you're not trying to exercise, awaken creativity, calm yourself, or even complete this exercise. Use the bullet points below to guide your writing afterward:

- Were you present to yourself and the world around you during the walk?

- Describe what you learned by taking the walk.

- What did you learn about the experience of being present? If you've experienced being present before, what does it feel like? How do you know you're being present?

- Have you experienced a difference in the way you work since you began jotting down your thoughts in these journaling pages? If so, describe the difference.

If you initially have difficulty answering these questions, be patient. Keep turning the questions over in your mind. Insights will come.

THE BENEFIT TO YOU: Writing about times you are present in your life is a gift you give to yourself. The more present you are in your life, the more of your self you can access in each interchange and activity. What's the overall benefit? With greater presence, you'll feel more alive and engaged in an enriched life, one that's full of meaning and purpose. ℘

Case Study

A recently hired employee's comments to a human resources manager after an orientation session:

"I need to talk to you. During the session, someone from your department explained the core values of this hospital. He said that good humor was one of your core values. I was struck by the way he explained it. He said the Greeks used to think of a person's temperament as the subtle mixing of four humors: blood, yellow bile, black bile, and phlegm. Depending on the way they mingled, people ended up with either sanguine, choleric, phlegmatic, or melancholic temperaments. Then he said, 'we think of "good humor" in much the same way. It influences how we work and we want every physician, employee, volunteer and contractor to have it.'

"Then he went on to say something that bothered me: 'This organization goes so far as to say that if you are not in good humor, you should act like you are.' I don't like pretense. When I'm in a lousy mood, I don't see why I should hide it. I want to be authentic. People will respect me for that. I don't expect others to be in a good mood all the time. I don't think they expect that of me either. Pretending about anything is a bad idea. Pretenders end up being phonies."

_____

_____

_____

_____

_____

LESSON: Nobody likes phonies, but to think that everyone should adjust to how we feel is immature and unrealistic. Everyone in health care needs to be able to put their immediate feelings in the background when they attend to patients' needs. The issue is one of maturity, professionalism, and service, not integrity.

Reward _No._ 2: Hearing _and_ Following Your Heart's Desires

The other reward for getting work fixation, addiction, or exhaustion under control is an ability to hear and then follow the murmurings of one's heart. At that point, people become committed to caring for themselves.

As they begin to live in the present, questions such as, "What do I really want to do?" and "What is asked of me at this time in my life?" will surface. The first arises because these individuals have become increasingly sensitive to their personal needs, and the second because they're less inclined now to constantly try to shape the world. They may begin to reminisce about the choices they made or didn't make, and how they landed in their current jobs. They may also wonder about their career choices.

In her journal, a former nurse wrote this about her employment and life choices:

"I am 56 years old and I know that I was lured into nursing. Ever since eighth grade, I wanted to be a nurse. Don't ask me why. I don't know. I was good at science and an A student in every subject. My father was, and still is, a biochemist. I took the pre-med track in college because that is what smart kids did. I dropped out of that track and followed my two best friends into nursing. It was cakewalk for me. I went straight from nursing school for a Ph.D. in nursing with a focus on ethics in health care.

"My first real job was not in patient care but in teaching. I got accepted into the tenure track at the university medical school where I stayed for seven years. I found the job deadening. Petty, petty, petty. The stuffiness was unbelievable. There came a point when I felt that I was becoming jaded and couldn't even stand myself.

"Much to the surprise of my colleagues, I resigned from the position at the university and moved with my husband to little town in Virginia. I've always loved horses. He grew up on a farm. We bought a small working farm and I thought about buying a horse. That led us to build a stable so we could board horses as a way of financing our venture. My nurse friends thought I was crazy to give up my secure position. I felt more excited than scared.

"Over the next 22 years, we built one of Virginia's small premier horse farms. Honest to god, when I think back on it, I never should have become a nurse. Teaching at the medical school was an even bigger mistake. I now

see that it was my father's unspoken dream for me. While there is no way in hell that I resent the path I took, I can now see that it was horses that I had loved ever since I was a little girl.

"While people at the university thought it was a mistake to give up my tenure, it was the second best move in my life. The first was marrying my husband. True, we're not rich, but I've learned something that is priceless: It takes a long time to listen to oneself. I was into what others wanted and hardly recognized my own dreams. What is extraordinary is that the drive that used to push me to excel has all but vanished. Today, even though I'm getting up there in years, I've got more energy than I've ever had. The difference is that I'm not driven like I was."

This woman realized how various forms of seduction—a father's approval, money, prestige, recognition—can shape our decision-making and lead us into careers or jobs that meet our immediate needs but not our heart's needs. It took time to quiet the voices of her father and peers, and consciously choose a personally meaningful work life: Raising horses, which she had loved since childhood. This new life was in harmony with her deepest needs yet also realistic and practical. Had she not changed course, would her heart have been peaceful? Probably not. More likely she would have become blind to life apart from work (fixated), driven (addicted), or empty and drained of energy (exhausted).

The heart is an apt metaphor to describe the process of consciously choosing a life that matches one's desires. In the normal buzz and swirl of daily life, people pay little attention to their physical heart. Only when their heart begins to falter or fail does it get their attention. A stethoscope isn't necessary to hear the heart of desire, our yearning. You can hear it beating when you're attentive to its longings. Just as life ends when the physical heart stops beating, so ends your inner life when you fail to follow your heart's desire.

There's a cost regardless of whether you maintain the status quo or risk a sensible jump into an unknown future. However, by jettisoning work fixation, addiction, or exhaustion, listening to and following your heart's desire will be easier precisely because you feel less rigid, driven, or empty.

On page 256, after Tip No. 25, we'll look at the consequences of not following your heart's desires.

Tip No. 25

to Help Ourselves

Set Aside Time *to* Explore Your Heart's Desires

Here's your opportunity to care for yourself by carving out time to reassess your life, work, and relationships. Take this time to understand what drives you and to more deeply clarify your passions, interests, and talents. Are you following these to their fullest? If not, why not?

Ideally, go to a quiet, retreat-like setting for a week to explore your yearnings and record your thoughts in this journal undisturbed. If that's not possible, try to set aside a day here and there for that purpose. Maybe this special time will take the form of slowing down to finally pay attention to a nagging preoccupation that has lingered in your consciousness for months or even years. Maybe you'll spend this time focusing on reflection, sharing your thoughts with others, or planning the steps that will bring you closer to the work that makes your heart sing. It's not important how you structure the time away; what matters is the process of seriously discerning your heart's desires.

In this effort, it's best to consult with a wise professional, a particularly insightful friend who speaks honestly, or your spouse or partner. You need to go beyond appearances and take an honest, realistic look at yourself and your life situation without a hasty critique.

Finding someone who will listen patiently and not jump to recommendations may be difficult. Opening up to that person may be even more challenging because work-fixated, -addicted, or -exhausted people often are self-reliant and unaccustomed to asking for help. Even though our approaches to work and life have gotten us into trouble, we still want to hold onto them.

In discerning your heart's desires, think about what you really want in life and if you're prepared to pay the price. That price could be leaving a lucrative job, shaking up your routine, making a change that leads to uncertainty in the short term, or walking away from a harmful relationship. As much as we welcome the renewed energy that accompanies moving toward alignment with our heart's desires, life upheaval can be tough. Although we may embrace it and feel empowered and exhilarated, there may also be a sense of loss and doubts about the new direction our life is taking. However, the long-term results and rewards of this journey are unmistakable and priceless.

THE BENEFIT TO YOU: Freedom! By giving yourself time and space to reflect only on your heart's desire, you set your life on a new course: A life rich with meaning and fulfillment. ♥

Case Study

FULFILLING A VISION

Allen is in his early thirties and has an endearing way about him. He's enthusiastic, sees the good in the world, and believes that justice will prevail when things go bad. You can't help liking the guy.

When he was in graduate school, he learned that infants born in his state had below-average birth weights compared with those born in other parts of the country. In one of his classes, he learned that this statistic was understandable because his state is largely rural and many women don't have access to prenatal care. As a father of three, Allen was shocked. He thought of his state as a forward-looking and health conscious place to live. Given his enthusiastic, can-do approach to life, it's not surprising that he wondered if he could do anything to improve things.

As CEO of his hospital's foundation, Allen asked the foundation board to award him a $25,000 grant. His proposed plan: Buy baby clothes, diapers, bottles, strollers, and other infant-care items, then open a store in the hospital's basement where he would offer them to mothers who came to the hospital for prenatal care. Each time they came for a check-up at the clinic, they would receive a coupon redeemable in the store he called "The Baby Boutique." The purchased goods would be tagged with coupon prices: baby bottles and diapers, one coupon; clothes, two coupons; a crib, three coupons; a stroller, four coupons; etc.

After the board agreed, Allen stocked the store with those supplies and he went out to neighborhood schools, community centers, playgrounds, churches, and synagogues and looked for young women who were obviously pregnant. He asked them if they had prenatal care. For a young male to get away with this gives you an idea of the kind of fellow he is. When Allen found a mom willing to admit that she didn't have prenatal care, he gave her a ticket entitling her to a free visit at the clinic of the highly respected local hospital. Women followed through and came for a visit received a coupon redeemable at "The Baby Boutique."

As you might imagine, word spread quickly among the moms who needed help. Allen didn't have to advertise.

What do you think happened to the birth weight of infants born to low-income women at that hospital during the first years of the program? They went up. Why? Probably because moms received prenatal care, although there aren't any studies to confirm this.

Allen has since begun programs called "Baby's First Ride" (to get infants into car seats) and "Boot Camp For Dads" (to get fathers involved in infant care).

Within each of us is a desire to rise to our highest calling. Many of us are filled with ideas about how to improve our workplace and communities. Implementing them and committing to follow our calling are often a matter of summoning courage. It takes a vision, planning, resources, and finally a leap of faith to fulfill our highest potential and act on our deepest calling.

YOUR INSIGHT:
_____

_____

_____

_____

LESSON: When we search within, we'll find our calling, a voice urging us to pursue a particular path. Perseverance and commitment to follow that voice can lead to living a more meaningful life and improving the quality of life for others.

The Consequences *of* Not Following Your Heart's Desires

What happens when, even though they know change is necessary, people with distorted, unhealthy behaviors stick to the well-worn path and remain trapped in the status quo? What if work addiction, fixation, or exhaustion seems to be a better option than an unpredictable future? From one perspective, little will happen. Life simply continues on the same trajectory.

However, there are consequences of staying trapped. If the heart is silenced, eventually these individuals will likely experience four consequences: the loss of creativity, depression, the demonization and idolization of others, and anxiety. Think of these as symptoms of a failure to heed the heart's whisperings rather than as signs of illness.

The Loss *of* Creativity

It may sound peculiar, but when a person arrives for therapy, most counselors see two patients, not just one: The me-who-has-died (things are not working out) and the me-who-is-alive (I need help). This split is common during times of significant personal change. Clients hold on to the me-who-has-died and know little about the future me-who-is-alive. In fact, most cling to the dead me for dear life, despite their discomfort. There's safety in familiarity. It's the therapist's job to help her let go of the dead me and embrace the person she is called to be.

At this point in her life, loss of creativity comes to the forefront, and no wonder. She has chosen to hold on to the dead me instead of following her heart's desires. Is creativity a characteristic of what has died? No. Creativity is a mark of the living, not the dead. The dead me can continue working dutifully, but her heart won't be invested or engaged in what she's doing. Although others may praise her as a steady, responsible, conscientious person, she knows she's lost her creativity and is merely pushing on.

People trapped in work fixation, addiction, or exhaustion are usually somewhat aware that beneath the busyness of their daily lives is an aliveness yearning to rise up. However, when they consider the cost of following their heart's desires, they pull back out of fear. Anticipating the loss of security, of a love relationship, of financial comfort, they cling to their familiar life despite the intense personal cost this choice brings. The old adage "stick with the devil you know" holds some truth.

Depression

There are various types of depression, each with numerous etiologies. For example, one is associated with the chemistry of the body and organs; it can be effectively treated with pharmaceuticals. A second type arises when someone perceives only a bleak future, giving rise to low spirits, melancholy, and negativity. An effective treatment in these cases is psychotherapy—especially cognitive-based approaches, sometimes in combination with medication. A third type of depression is linked to past experiences, such as childhood abuse or combat-related post-traumatic stress disorder. It is particularly long lasting and difficult to treat.

The depression that occurs when people overlook their heart's desires is a kind of heaviness, as if they were weighted down, or de-pressed. The heaviness is a result of having to push through life rather than being propelled by passion, energy, and a deep belief that what they're doing is right and meaningful. Although nonclinical, this kind of depression is no less real than clinical depression and is the direct result of ignoring one's calling.

The Demonization *and* Idolization *of* Others

Picasso once humorously quipped, "When I was a child, my mother said to me, 'If you become a soldier, you'll be a general. If you become a monk, you'll end up as the pope.' Instead I became a painter and wound up as Picasso."[4]

If, unlike Picasso, someone denies their heart's desire and becomes the person others expect her to be, she will see others in an overly positive or overly negative light. That's because she's inclined to blame others for her failure to follow her own dreams and fulfill her own expectations. She views others as demons or she idolizes them. Here's an example of how demonization and idolization work:

A long-time friend of mine holds what has become a routine job in the accounts payable department at our local hospital. She knows she needs a more stimulating job at this time in her life but feels she can't leave her position because she'd lose the generous benefits she has accrued over the years, including a high salary and many banked vacation days. Truth be known, she values her paid time off more than her ample compensation.

Rather than talk about her feelings of being trapped, she criticizes others. She says, "The spirit of the office has taken a tumble. I can't stand it. The problem is our new manager. He is weak. They need to get rid of him. My vote is for Jane, our previous manager. She is direct, strong, and a go-getter. This new guy's a wimp." I've heard her express these sentiments more than once.

Because my friend feels imprisoned by her comfortable perks, she unconsciously redirects her energies onto others, demonizing the new manager as weak and idolizing the previous manager as strong. I know all three players in this drama; both managers are highly competent. Jane doesn't hold that job anymore because she found the responsibilities distasteful. "I was good at it, but I really didn't like being a manager," she said. The person with a problem is my friend. She needs the courage to live her own life.

Surrendering to fear—of what the future holds, of who they'll become if they follow their heart—is one of the most difficult challenges people encounter as they become who they are called to be. Fear is nearly always the biggest obstacle—fear of loss, fear of disappointing others, fear of failure, fear of success, fear of rejection, fear of being less than our imagined self. Your most important task is gaining the strength to face your fears.

Anxiety

Anxiety arises when someone feels threatened by something unknown, such as a possible event or action in the future. Fear arises when someone feels threatened by something tangible. For example, one time I became afraid while crossing Second Avenue in Manhattan. When the light turned yellow, I was too far out in the middle of the wide street to turn back but too far from the other side to reach it before the light in my direction turned red. I knew what threatened me and was realistically and understandably frightened. In contrast, people who feel anxious don't know what's causing their anxiety. If you ask them why they feel anxious, they are being honest when they say that they do not know.

Let's explore what triggers anxiety, a fear of the unknown. This "unknown" can be an external event or our failure to own and embrace the person we are called to become. To better understand how the call to pursue a new work direction can make people anxious, let's think of ourselves as being the shape of a sphere with multiple layers. There is a shiny outer layer that others see. They recognize us as a competent nurse, physician, lab tech, housekeeper, engineer, or lawyer. The uniform or stethoscope confirms our identity and their impression of us. Despite its shine, that outer layer is thin, fragile, and easily broken.

Just beneath our sphere's gleaming surface is a thick layer hidden from public view—perhaps from ourselves, too. It influences every action we take, every word we utter, every thought we have. It even influences our relationships significantly. We'll call this inner layer "gook." It's filled with the largely negative feelings we've collected over the years, such as inadequacy, along with the thoughts and experiences we try to repress out of a concern that our reputation and self-esteem will be injured if others see them. We are haunted by the expectation that others will reject us if they see our gook. Anxiety mounts from our uncertainty and insecurity.

That inner layer affects our fragile outer selves whether we acknowledge it or not. Denying the inner layer's existence makes us its unwitting puppet; our feelings, actions, and choices are dictated by these forces that we refuse to acknowledge and own, which is why it's in our own best interests to explore those dark feelings and beliefs. An experience I had not so long ago illustrates this dynamic:

I was staying in a New York City hotel the night before making a minor presentation to an organization's annual meeting. Around 2 a.m., I awoke with a start, realizing out of the blue that I had not changed an error on one of my presentation slides. The problem was I had sent the file to the hotel's computer technician before I left my office to fly to the meeting. My contract with the organization stipulated that no changes to the file could be made once it was sent.

"What a fool you are!" I scolded myself during those early morning hours. "You should have had someone check that file last week. That slide will be one more indication to everyone just how incompetent you are." My self-recrimination went further. "Why did you accept this invitation to speak in the first place? You know you've got enough on your plate." Self-blame and anxiety mounted.

This is an example of the gook layer breaking through my outwardly shiny, competent self. By the time I arrived to make my presentation nine hours later, I had my act together. Conference participants saw only the professional I claim to be. I had tightly sealed and polished the crack that allowed the gook to ooze to the surface during the night.

Within your sphere but beneath the gook layer is a smaller sphere that's as bright and vibrant as the gook is dark and murky. Call it "the me I am conscious of being" or the "I" sphere. Here there is warmth, even sacredness. It's the place where I honestly know I'm a good and honest person. For the religious, it's where the divine dwells. The following scenario shows how the

"I" sphere plays a critical role in self-discovery:

You had a disagreement with a colleague at work. During a heated exchange, she became incensed because she thinks you justify your actions rather than take responsibility for making a mistake. "You're incredibly arrogant," she blurts out. Understandably defensive, you spontaneously deny her devaluing opinion. You know you're not arrogant. She's wrong. No one else has ever said this about you.

Later at home, her words continue to rankle. "Why does she think I'm arrogant?" you ask yourself. "I'm not." You become preoccupied trying to answer this question and figure out why you feel uncomfortable around her.

A few months pass. Since that unsettling exchange, you've done some soul searching. You openly and honestly talked about the incident with a trusted friend who, instead of taking sides, remarked almost casually, "Sure, sometimes you are a little arrogant. I've always known that. Many of us show that ugly streak now and then."

Coming from your friend, the words sound different. Now you can slowly acknowledge, at least to yourself, that indeed you're arrogant at times. "Funny. My friend said she's always known that about me. And she's still my friend!" The bright "I" sphere buried deep within the gook has expanded to include arrogance as one of the things you know about yourself. That thought didn't add anything that wasn't already there. The colleague at work had simply helped nudge it into your consciousness, which enabled you to recognize and accept it as a part of who you are.

People feel particularly anxious in times of transition. It's a common, normal, expected response—an indication that someone is being called to become comfortable with the person she aspires to be. Such anxiety is an invitation to surrender to the me-who-is-alive—what I am becoming—and let go of the me-who-has-died.

A Reflection

Job Interviews

Now and again for any number of reasons, we must go through job interviews. We may want a job that offers new possibilities within the same organization. At other times we're interested in a job in another hospital, nursing home, office, or setting. During job searches emotions run high. Questions like, "Did I present myself well?" "Do I have the competencies they are looking for?" "Do I really have a chance to land the job?" "I know that first impressions are important. Will they like me?" Those are questions that I have had. Perhaps you have had similar ones.

My wife, infinitely more sagacious than I am in these matters, chuckles at my anxiety. "Just be yourself," she says. "If you get the job, fine. If not, fine! You've got to be yourself. If not, you'll never be at peace with yourself nor will you find the right job."

At first, her advice seems simplistic. However, when I look back on my experience, she's right. Sometimes we feel as if we can only bring part of ourselves to work—say the technical and proficient side of ourselves—and something would be wrong if other parts of ourselves were exposed at work, like our inner emotional, heart side.

Richard Rohr writes, "It's not just gay people who have to come out of their closets. We're all in our closets. They've just given us a good metaphor for what we all have to do. We're all afraid to come out of our various closets. It's not the need to be outrageous or rebellious. It's so much better than that."

What is the "it" that is so much better? Richard Rohr, writes from the perspective of spirituality. The "it" is "…permission to be that image and likeness of God that you really are. You are unlike any other image or likeness." Similar to my wife, he encourages us to be ourselves and not to fear the consequences.

Maybe you feel, as I have in the past, that the counsel to be ourselves is a little too slick or that it falls into the realm of pop psychology. If that is how you feel, remember the insight of e.e. cummings who had something to say about the need to be ourselves: "To be nobody but yourself in a world which is doing its best, night and day, to make you everybody else means to fight the hardest battle which any human being can fight; and never stop fighting."

I'm not sure that the effort to be ourselves requires a fight, but it involves continual effort, a degree of self awareness, and a continued openness to change even if it means overcoming our fears. Would you agree?

To work within health care is a gift. It seems as if every experience, including a job interview, presents us with the opportunity to learn about ourselves. What have you recently learned about the challenges of either changing jobs or remaining in your job as you go about caring for others? ♥

Notes ～

Notes

Notes ➴

Notes

Notes

Finding *the* Right Work

"To live is to choose. But to choose well, you must know who you are and what you stand for, where you want to go and why you want to get there."

KOFI ANNAN, 7TH SECRETARY-GENERAL OF THE UNITED

NATIONS, 2001 NOBEL PEACE PRIZE RECIPIENT

Once you've slowed the pace of your life and honestly listened to your deeper yearning, hopes, and dreams of more enriched, meaningful work, expect to face unsettling questions that a pattern of overwork either silenced or denied. You may ask yourself: Am I in the right job? If not, how do I find it?

In 2010, the employment Web site Monster.com ran a full-page add in *The New York Times* that read, "You don't really 'find' a job. You identify, evaluate, and seize the opportunity."[1] Monster.com helps job seekers take control, seize the moment, and jump. The following two experiences—time I spent with a colleague and a conversation I overheard at the local Starbucks—illustrate how the simple but deep desire to uncover and follow our yearning can take us to new, unexpected places and open us to uncharted opportunities.

In looking for the right job, the colleague who spent a weekend at my home, takes a more evolutionary approach than Monster.com. He hasn't found that job yet, but he keeps his ear to the ground and believes one will come along. "That's when I'll jump," he said.

When he was younger, he worked as a consultant at a company that helped employees deal with organizational change. He liked the job and thought he did good work, but he was uncomfortable with the sales aspect, recalling, "I felt that I had to sell myself. That was distasteful and went against my personal beliefs. I don't want to keep telling people about how good I am and how I can help their organization."

He left and became a mentor and adviser at a pastoral counseling center—and didn't like that job either. "I listened to people's problems all day long. Most of them were marital and that got me down." Today he moonlights as a part-time adjunct professor at a local college, a job that isn't particularly satisfying. "I need something really challenging." He thinks his episodic depression is directly related to his inability to find the right employment.

That weekend, we had some significant conversations as well as fun. Before he and his wife headed home on Sunday afternoon, he went out of his way to tell me several times how helpful the visit had been. "My spirits are lifted," he said. "Now I feel that I'm on the right track."

I didn't know what "on the right track" meant, but I was glad he felt better. The guidance I offered also had an unintended consequence. It made me feel useful and gave me satisfaction knowing I'd been helpful.

The second experience occurred on Monday. One of my routines is to rise early, find a soft chair at Starbucks, nurse a cup of coffee, and peruse the morning paper. A half-dozen other men do the same. The anonymous group members greet each other by looking up and nodding, nothing more. No one utters a word. The only thing we seem to have in common is an appreciation of coffee and the shared values of privacy and quiet.

The stillness was broken that day when a fellow came up to the man sitting next to me, excused himself, said he was from Ann Arbor, Michigan, and asked if he'd be willing to talk. To my surprise, he said, "Sure." Up to then, I'd never heard him speak.

The visitor began by saying he came to Santa Fe because he'd had the impression he would find a "unique community where people were not just interested in money but in each other." He was disappointed. In his opinion, Santa Fe was quaint but no different from other commercialized towns. He wanted to know if my reading companion could suggest someplace else.

"What are you are looking for?" my normally silent groupie asked.

"Like I said before, a place that's different. A place where people are connected. A place where I fit in."

"Have you visited Taos? It's less developed than Santa Fe and is an art community."

"Yes, nothing special there."

"How about southern New Mexico? There are only small towns in that part of the state. Families date back hundreds of years. They don't move. I think you'll find them connected."

"Maybe. Sounds far away, but I'll give that a try."

The psychologist in me started to analyze the conversation and diagnose the traveler's behavior. Was he just looking for more intimate relationships? Was he searching for a commune-like place, as are many other young people who come to Santa Fe? Was he lonely? Maybe he was in the gregarious stage of a hyper-manic. Was he a writer in search of a story or a novelist looking for real-life dialogue to incorporate into his latest novel? Was he a con artist in the first stage of wooing a victim? My brain raced among the possibilities.

While driving home, I thought about the similarities between the colleague who had visited me and this stranger. Both were looking for something—my colleague a meaningful job, the young man a community. Both seemed to believe that if they got what they wanted, their yearning would be satisfied.

Long ago I read advice from the Austrian poet Rainer Maria Rilke to a young man who was looking outside himself for answers to questions he found disturbing:

You ask whether your poems are good. You send them to publishers; you compare them with other poems; you are disturbed when certain publishers reject your attempts. Well, now, since you have given me permission to advise you, I suggest that you give all that up. You are looking outward and, above all else, that you must not do now. No one can advise and help you, no one.

There is only one way: Go within. Search for the cause, find the impetus that bids you write. Put it to this test: Does it stretch out its roots in the deepest place of your heart? Can you avow that you would die if you were forbidden to write? Above all, in the most silent hour of your night, ask yourself this: Must I write? Dig deep into yourself for a true answer. And if it should ring its assent, if you can confidently meet this serious question with a simple, "I must," then build your life upon it. It has become your necessity. Your life, in even the most mundane and least significant hour, must become a sign, a testimony to this urge.[2]

Rilke's suggestion to "go within" is yet another approach to finding the right job. Is it wise advice for my colleague or for the traveler at Starbucks? Is there a right job for you or me?

In fact, no job is so well-suited to a person's interests and abilities that he will never need to search again. As the philosophers remind us, we're never finished; we're always on our way, a work in progress. The most you or I can say is that this job is a good fit for me at this point in my life.

Case Study

A recent retiree describes his struggles:

"During midlife, I ended my clinical practice as a psychologist, let my licenses expire, and accepted the invitation to become a hospital executive. Last year, I retired from that position after a dozen years. My wife and I have now relocated. Yesterday my next-door neighbor asked me, 'What do you do?'

"I didn't know how to answer. To say that I was a psychologist or a hospital executive wouldn't have answered his question. I'm no longer either. He wanted to know what I do now. I was hesitant to say that I'm retired. For some reason, the words stick in my mouth.

.

"This is the seventh decade of my life. I have worked in dedicated and successful ways for years. Isn't it time for me to step apart from the workaday world, relax a little, and think of how I want to use the remaining years? That's what my wife thinks. I feel a little differently; I need a title other than 'retired.'

"Being retired is like being a former something-or-other. Former teachers, technicians, physicians, health care professionals, government workers, and military people all talk that way. The dictionary links retirement with the process of disengaging. That's not appealing to me. When others tell me to take care of myself, I know that they are well intentioned, but they don't know me. I've always taken care of myself even in high-pressured jobs. If retirement means nothing more than taking care of myself, withdrawing from life, or holding on to a past identity, I want no part of it. Neither do I want to be one of those retirees doing volunteer work. I want to do something meaningful and get paid for it!"

YOUR INSIGHT:

_____

_____

_____

_____

_____

LESSON: All of us are inevitably in transition and invited to become more than we are. Having a job or profession is one thing; being engaged in meaningful activities is another.

For years I was a member of the De La Salle Brothers, a Roman Catholic religious teaching congregation that at the time numbered about 18,000 monks worldwide. The Brothers are celibate, live in communities of men, and make vows of chastity, poverty, and obedience. The group is particularly sensitive to poverty around the globe and the needs of disadvantaged youth. Believing that education is the way out of poverty, members dedicate themselves to establishing schools and teaching youngsters. I've never met a more generous group of individuals.

As fortune would have it, I attended graduate school and lived apart from the Brothers for several years. There I fell in love with a classmate. I can't easily explain the conflict that followed. I was genuinely happy as a Brother and convinced that my involvement in a group dedicated to helping children escape poverty was a valuable way to spend my life. Many Brothers were my friends and I felt deeply attached to them and the congregation. I also admired the way they lived. Because they shared their resources, each Brother had incredible opportunities to pursue continuing education and travel. It was a life-giving way to live.

However, I couldn't deny my feelings for the woman I loved. I imagined a significantly different future for myself—marriage, children, making a home together. The excitement was palpable. So was the split in my heart. Although I wasn't totally conscious of what was happening, a part of me was dying and another part coming alive. (Recall from Chapter 7 the me-who-has-died and the me-who-is-alive.) The dissonance between these two selves was undeniable. It took years for me to decide what to do; eventually I left the De La Salle Brothers and married—the best decision I ever made. That was 25 years ago. Would you understand if I said that becoming a Brother at age 19 was also the best decision I ever made? I live with gratitude for having made both choices.

I'd be surprised if many readers haven't also experienced the pull of competing loves. They are times of growth, albeit painful times.

Here is another example of how no job is a perfect fit forever. Picture a young man who begins working as a hospital lab technician after he graduates with an associate degree from the local college. He may say to himself at the time, "It's the perfect job, it's meaningful, I can help people, it pays enough, I'm happy. It's a dream come true." Three years later, after his second child is born, it may not be perfect anymore. The pay isn't adequate to support his income requirements and the hours conflict with the demands he faces as a father with young children.

Viktor Frankl, the Austrian neurologist and psychiatrist, had another perspective on the "right job:"

No one occupation is the sole road to salvation. It is true that many persons, mostly those with a neurotic tinge, insist that they could have fulfilled themselves if only they had gone into a different occupation. But that assertion is either a misunderstanding of what the occupation means, or is self-deception. If there are cases where the actual occupation does not allow a sense of fulfillment to arise, the fault is in the person, not in the work. The work in itself does not make the person indispensable and irreplaceable; it only gives him the chance to be so.[3]

Frankl's thoughts are particularly cogent because he formulated them as a Holocaust prisoner who had been stripped of everything valuable—the people he loved as well as his identity, work, power, and possessions.

Another colleague of mine also has been engaged in the never-ending process of finding the right job. A physician who trained at prestigious medical schools, he gave up a promising career in the United States to go with his wife to Tanzania as a medical missionary of the Lutheran Church. The couple established a small clinic there. Its services soon expanded to include AIDS patients, and now it cares for more than 1,600 hospice patients. Increasing numbers of physicians and nurses from the United States and Europe have volunteered to help him train African caregivers. Two years ago, a second facility opened—this one a state-of-the-art hospital. He is somewhat of a modern-day Albert Schweitzer, the German theologian, physician, and medical missionary who worked in west central Africa in the twentieth century. My colleague said this of his career choices and trajectory:

"I always wanted to be a medical missionary. It is not that I had some plan and then set about building what I had envisioned. It was much more ordinary. I liked medicine and knew that I wanted to help those in need, particularly those most in need. I had no idea that I would stay here 30 years, that we would raise our three children here, and that this work would expand the way it has.

"What is extraordinary is the way that the work envelops you. It makes its demands and you have an opportunity to say either yes to what is asked

of you or to withdraw. As you say yes, more of you gets pulled into the work. It becomes a commitment. Instead of doing this for a set time or withholding a part of yourself, every corner of your being is touched. I'm here not only as a person with the technical training of a physician and administrator, but all of me is here. I doubt if many people can understand what I am talking about unless they've known the experience of bringing every fiber of their being to some undertaking. I think that is what gives my wife and I the energy we have. It's more than a job. While life here has at times been difficult and frightening, it's become a commitment."

While this man lives what many would consider to be a near heroic life, the fact is that many people have meaningful jobs to which they are fully committed They may work as nurses or parents, in the creative arts or business, as teachers, researchers, child care providers, or salesmen. The defining characteristic of any commitment is the degree to which it engages the whole person over a lifetime. When one is whole-heartedly involved in work, it is actually an antidote to overwork because one's heart is fully engaged and fulfilled. A commitment or calling may be manifested through a string of different jobs throughout one's life, with each job allowing the expression of a different talent or skill.

If there's such a thing as the "right job," I suspect it has something to do with following one's calling. Callings are often associated with religion. In the Bible, God called Abraham.

Some faith communities say their members are called to do missionary work. A Jewish man may feel called to become a rabbi. A young woman may feel called to the ministry. What's asked of them is linked with what they feel God asks of them. This places their commitment in the context of the sacred.

The experience of being called is also part of everyday secular life. A vocation is simply listening and responding to what we are genuinely drawn to do. Many of us are like the woman in Chapter 7 who responded to a series of callings, first as a nurse, then as a university professor, then as a horse breeder in Virginia. Once people learn to be present, they begin to experience life as a series of callings precisely because they can hear what is asked of them. Consider this man's journey:

"I'm one of those fellows you would call a workaholic. By profession I'm an accountant. Right out of school as a young 23 year old, I got a position with a New York accounting firm but worked out of San Francisco. When you take that kind of position, you expect to work 75-hour weeks. That's what every newly hired employee in that company did. It took me eight years to make partner. As you can see from where we live today, I've done well.

"The thing that really changed my life around was my decision to go to the playground on the weekend with my youngest child. One day, Cherie was playing with her best friend, another 10 year old, whose father had died while serving in Afghanistan. During a chance conversation with the

girl's mother, I learned that the youth association needed someone to coach the girl's soccer team. 'You don't need to know much about soccer,' she said. 'You just need to know the rules and help the kids play together. They're all 10 or 12 year olds. They're all from the army base. It's a great group of kids.'

"When she said the girls only play Saturday and Sunday mornings, I didn't have much of an excuse about work interfering (except for my self-imposed, inner drive as a workaholic), so I told her I'd think about it. I decided that the personal fulfillment I'd get from being a coach far outweighed whatever satisfaction I was trying to gain from my workaholic lifestyle. That was two years ago and I'm still coaching. I enjoy it even though Cherie is now too old for that group of kids.

"They also got me to serve on the board of the rec center. You know how boards work. That got me into fundraising.

"The financial challenges were easy to handle. What was a bummer was seeing the toll it takes on kids when a parent is away for a year, sometimes more, and the stress that the spouse feels when left behind.

"I can tell you that being a volunteer at the rec center has changed the way I think about things. The biggest change is that I'm less engaged at my real job. I don't mean that I'm slacking off. I'm not. I'm just thinking more about things and wondering about what others need. My wife keeps saying that we already have enough. She thinks it's time we start thinking about others. I feel the same way now."

This man, like the physician in Tanzania and the woman with a Virginia horse farm, are all in the process of finding the right job—that is, merging their heart's desires with the needs around them. They mirror the way most of us awaken to a higher calling and find jobs that fit. In the words of Carl Frederick Buechner, an American writer and theologian, "The place God calls you to is the place where your deep gladness and the world's deep hunger meet."[3b]

Case Study

THE MEANINGFULNESS OF A CALLING

Last week I was invited to a planning session to create a workshop at our hospital on how to find and hold meaningful employment. Some participants thought the question wasn't relevant for people in health care, along the lines of "everyone knows that any job in health care is meaningful." One person said the question shouldn't be raised: "Nurses will start thinking about changing jobs. We don't need that kind of unrest."

The conversation got me thinking about Viktor Frankl, the Holocaust survivor. Amid the unimaginable brutality of a death camp, Frankl awakened to the fact that he had a responsibility to survive and be of help to others by teaching and writing as a professional. Woe to him, he thought, if he succumbed to thinking that his life had lost its meaning. Frankl would teach that all of us must listen to what is asked of us in life as we simultaneously consider how we want to direct our lives.

Sam Keen, the philosophy and religion professor, wrote: "A society in which vocation and job are separated gradually creates an economy that is often devoid of spirit, one that frequently fills our pocketbooks at the cost of emptying our souls."[3a] I hope participants in the meaningful employment workshop at our hospital have time to think about themselves as being called or as being a calling. Such awareness changes our presence—how we live and interact at work and in our private lives.

YOUR INSIGHT:

_____

_____

_____

_____

_____

LESSON: Work can provide deep meaning in our lives, not simply a means to a paycheck. Do you "have" a calling? Do you think you "are" your calling?

If we listen to the inner voices previously muffled under the weight of work addiction, fixation, or exhaustion, three insights emerge:

One, if we heed what's asked of us in life, a sense of peace and well-being will follow. The truth of Viktor Frankl's words—"The search for the quintessential job is as futile as asking a chess master what is the most perfect move in chess"[4]—becomes evident. Just as a chess master's every move depends on the ever-changing position of the queen, knights, bishops, rooks, and pawns, so our choices depend on the situation at any given time, which may be as necessary and commonplace as caring for an aging parent, adjusting to an unplanned birth, returning to school, entering politics, becoming a manager, or continuing on the path we've already chosen. My calling isn't yours and yours isn't mine.

Two, we will become comfortable with the realization that we're unfinished personally and professionally. "Any job is a point along the way after which there is another point!" wrote Thomas Moore, the award-winning author and lecturer on spirituality. "Your sense of what you are meant to do with your life has to remain open-ended, no matter how much or how little you feel you have accomplished. You never know fully what you are called to do."[4a] Or, I would add, who you are called to become.

Three, we will experience what it means to be irreplaceable and indispensable because every occupation provides the opportunity for a person to discover her value. "The indispensability and irreplaceability, the singularity and uniqueness issue from the person...who is doing the work and on the manner in which s/he is doing it, not on the job itself," [5] Frankl wrote.

Landing the right job involves more than an outward search. At some point, the search turns inward. What is life asking of us? Who are we are called to become? The journey never ends. By not follow our calling, we can expect a loss of creativity, depression, the demonization and idolization of others, and anxiety. If we invite and embrace the journey, we are filled with gratitude for past experiences, anticipation of the future's unborn potential, and a quiet, unshakable satisfaction that comes from living an authentic life.

A Reflection

OUR WORK AS A CALLING

Yesterday I had the good fortune to have a conversation with a woman who recently retired from a career in nursing. For years, she was a staff nurse at a leading university hospital in the Midwest and then served as the chief nursing officer and administrator at an eminent health system in New England. During the conversation she said something about nurses and nursing that got me thinking about health care providers who are not nurses.

She said that she thought it is almost impossible to work as a nurse, particularly within settings where you work directly with ill patients, and not be forced to face some of life's most profound questions. "Nurses see birth and death, grace and misfortune, people at their best and worst, success and failure, almost every day. You can't help but be affected." Then she added, "Almost every nurse knows exactly what I'm talking about. It is what makes them good nurses. They are not afraid of life, know that the patient for whom they care at the moment is most important, and that everything else is secondary."

I wondered if that was true. How can nurses have that kind of presence to patients in the world of high tech health care? Doesn't she know about paperwork, patient staff ratios, and the pace of the workday? So I asked her, "Is what you are saying really the way things are? Can nurses today be present to their patients in the way you describe?"

"Absolutely. This has been my experience. Some come into nursing with that kind of motivation from the get go. Some have had the desire to be a nurse from their youth. They see nursing as a calling. The numbers are greater than you think. That is why so many nurses simply want to nurse patients one on one.

Then there are those who enter nursing because they think of it as a stable, worthwhile career. They are looking for job security. Curiously, they are soon faced with patient experiences that leave them reflective. They see life in all of its mystery. It's not long before they too, experience their profession as a calling. Many get to feel this way about their profession.

And then there are some nurses who are trapped in the profession. They are shut down in the face of its demands and challenges. They grow cold. The good pay and doable hours keep them stuck. These people can do immense harm."

While I know many nurses, I am not a nurse so I cannot comment on this woman's observations regarding her profession. Yet her thoughts lead me to think about the experience of those of us in health care who are not at the bedside. What is it that keeps us engaged? I am willing to bet that our experience is similar to that of the nurses. We feel as if our work is a calling.

Do you think that most who work in health care settings would agree with the following thought of Henri Nouwen?

Let us not underestimate how hard it is to be compassionate. Compassion is hard because it requires the inner disposition to go with others to places where they are weak, vulnerable, lonely, and broken. But this is not our spontaneous response to suffering. What we desire most is to do away with suffering by fleeing from it or finding a quick cure for it. ❧

Notes

Notes ⌣

Notes ⤝

Notes ~

9

Reflections *for*
Healing *with* Heart

"Our power lies in our small
daily choices, one after another,
to create eternal ripples of
a life well lived."

MOLLIE MARTI

The following reflections are written for health care professionals. They are similar to the reflections found in the award-winning book, *Healing with Heart: Inspirations for Health Care Professionals*, written by Martin Helldorfer and Terri Moss. Read these reflections to become inspired and refresh your soul. Read them in a quiet moment before or after work, or even in the middle of one of those tense, crazy days when taking time apart seems like the last thing you should do. Try making it the first.

Read these at team meetings, management retreats or just to yourself. Use them to start discussions, connect with one another, or simply to reconnect with yourself.

A Reflection

NURSES VS. HOSPITALS: WHY WORK IN HEALTH CARE?

Residents of my small town woke up to see the newspaper's front page headlines, "Nurses' Firings Shed Light On Union, Hospital Rift." The previous day the headlines were equally unsettling. "Lawsuit: Nurses Work Through Lunch With No Pay." Last week the paper ran another front-page story that exposed how the hospital was "slapped with a $10.3M penalty in bed sore lawsuit." I bet you've seen similar headlines at one time or another where you live.

The letters to the editor were strident as you might expect. Many readers were surprised that nurses complained about having to work through their lunch hours without pay. Managers insisted that nurses should take time for lunch and additional periodic breaks during their shifts and that the quality of patient care depended on taking those breathers. The unions wanted the hospital to award back pay for contract violations. Executives would not comment. Lawmakers weighed in on the side of laid off employees noting how jobs were needed in the community and no one should be laid off except for the most serious reasons.

With headlines and issues like these, who would want to work in health care? I do. Likely, you do as well.

I do not know why you are engaged in patient care—either directly or in support of those at the bedside—but I can tell you why I am. It is because I know of no other profession, job, career or calling, that is more needed, valued, or important. You do not learn how profound the value of this work is from books. It is grasped when either you or a loved one is ill and in need of care. In that moment, the gift of a caregiver who brings a healing presence to whatever it is they do—whether nurse, phlebotomist, housekeeper, aide, physician, respiratory therapist, or plumber—becomes an unforgettable memory. We want to be that kind of person.

Today, health care is fast paced, high tech, and results oriented. It is also a business. At times there are serious labor issues and unpleasant tensions between groups and individuals. Because of this it is all the more important to remember why it is we work within health care. To forget one's heart, memory, or dreams is to lose perspective. To bring them to work changes everything.

"When I think about all the patients and their loved ones that I have worked with over the years, I know most of them don't remember me nor I them. But I do know that I gave a little piece of myself to each of them and they to me, and those threads make up the beautiful tapestry in my mind that is my career in nursing."
—Donna Wilk Cardillo, RN

Today, I will reflect on why I do what I do. Is this my calling? I'll bring my heart, my presence to work. ❧

A Reflection

Why Do We Work?

If research is accurate, most of us seek employment because we need the money to care for our children, pay the rent or mortgage, put food on the table, make car payments, and to do all the things necessary to maintain a desired life style. Those responsibilities are real and cannot be avoided. Is the research accurate? Are they the reasons that you work?

Perhaps you heard Bill Moyers interview John Reed, the former Chairman of the Board of Citigroup and currently the President of the Massachusetts Institute of Technology. Somewhat playfully but with intent, Reed asked Moyers if he knew why we had brakes on our cars. Moyers thought for a second and quipped, "Obviously, to stop." Reed's response was surprising, "No, we have them so we can go faster. If we didn't have them we would be afraid to move. The more we have them, the faster we can go!"

Have you thought of brakes in that way? I haven't. It is a fresh perspective and a little different from our everyday way of thinking. I wonder if it would be helpful to turn our usual way of thinking on its head when we think about why we work in health care.

While work provides the dollars we need to live, is that the end of the story? I think not. If brakes exist to help us go faster, the work of caring for others, while it sometimes involves demanding responsibilities, can actually help us to live more reflectively. The fact is it is difficult to see a baby born, a breast removed, or a life lost or saved, without becoming reflective. Who is not affected by working in an emergency department, hospice, Alzheimer's unit, nursing home, or home health agency?

Though a paycheck may be one incentive to work within a health care setting, a more telling reason is that our hearts are touched by the needs of our patients. Once touched by others' needs, our hearts are warmed. It is then that money is less of a motivating force. Helen Keller, who could neither hear nor see, had a warmed heart. In her words, "The world is full of suffering, it is also full of overcoming it." That is what caregivers are about.

Understanding the motivation of the majority of caregivers lies in recognizing their endless sensitivity to those who suffer and their awe of the unfathomable drama of being human. They would agree with Pierre Teilhard de Chardin:

"The most satisfying thing in life is to have been able to give a large part of oneself to others."

Would you agree?

Some caregivers feel overwhelmed by the thought of attempting to meet the endless needs of patients. As a result, their hearts are hardened in an effort to protect themselves. For others, the suffering, fears, and needs of patients strengthens—rather than diminishes—their desire to be of service.

Why do you work as you do? I would be surprised if it were merely for its financial rewards.

When I reflect on whether I would do my job even if I didn't get paid, I'm opening my mind to what I can do to make my work more meaningful. Starting right now, I will consider what I can do to add meaning and purpose to my work. ♥

A Reflection

VISITORS

Have you ever had the experience of being at the bedside of a seriously ill or dying patient surrounded by as many as twelve family members? I have not, yet I know people who have.

One instance occurred last week. A nurse spoke of being in the room where a dying man was surrounded by his three children and nine loved ones. Evidently, such a large number violated the policy that limited the number of visitors "to the immediate family, not to exceed three at a time." The policy also stated that exceptions could be made at the discretion of the nursing staff.

In this particular situation, the charge nurse decided to enforce the policy. As a result, the patient's primary nurse was asked to go into the room to tell the family about the policy. The nurse was clearly uncomfortable. Nevertheless she went into the room to tell them that all but three would have to leave.

The patient began to cry. He asked that his wife and two daughters, one of whom was a retired nurse, stay with him. As the visitors filed out, they gathered in the waiting area just a few steps away from the patient's room. The nurse who had to enforce the rule followed them. She told me that she was as uncomfortable with the decision as those who were asked to leave the bedside. However, as awkward as she felt, she sat down with the visitors in the waiting room. Today she refers to that situation as her "ah ha" experience.

One of the visiting family members, a woman who appeared to be in her early twenties, spoke directly to the nurse. Her words, as the nurse remembers, were, "You people think that we are the visitors to this place. You've got it all wrong. We've been a family for all 71 years of my father's life. You people should remember that you are visiting us."

The nurse said she was shocked by that woman's perspective. She never thought of herself as a visitor to patients and their families. Rather, they were visitors to the hospital, the place where she was at home.

As a result of the experience in the waiting room, she said that she began to think anew about her role as a caregiver. What if she really were a visitor, something of a guest, maybe even an intruder, in the life of a family? Would that attitudinal shift make a difference in the way she viewed families and cared for patients?

Her answer to that question was an unqualified yes. "It's one of the most important learning experiences I've ever had. It has made me gentler, more understanding, and immensely more inquisitive. I know that it has made me more respectful."

Have you ever thought about who is visiting whom in a nursing home, hospital, or office? If so, what have you learned?

I will open my mind to a new perspective by turning life upside down and examining it. Is this the right thing to do? Is this the most helpful, healing way to approach my patients, my work? I welcome every experience as an opportunity to examine my assumptions and consider a new way. ♥

A Reflection

The Titanic and the World Trade Center

This week the papers and news channels are filled with continuing stories about the sinking of the Titanic and the bombing of the World Trade Center that happened well over a decade ago. Why is there such interest in these particular stories? There have certainly been more tragic stories where the loss of life has been even greater. It is understandable to honor the one hundredth anniversary of the sinking of the Titanic with news stories. But why is there so much press about the World Trade Center? Is it because of the controversy surrounding the building of a memorial at Ground Zero? And why are the two tragedies linked? Is it because the stories make interesting copy for journalists?

I think those of us who work in health care have a hunch. It has to do with the mystery of life—something you and I face when caring for patients and something all of us learn from tragedies such as these. Think about it for a moment. In both tragedies, many of the people in the World Trade Center and on the Titanic, knew that death was imminent. Have you heard the final phone messages of those who called from the planes? Have you read some of the emails and text messages sent by those trapped in the World Trade Center before it collapsed? Have you read the stories of survivors of the Titanic? One woman on the Titanic chose to stay with her husband on the sinking ship rather than get in a lifeboat. Sure there are some stories of ugliness and violence in those terrifying final moments, but the overwhelming number of documented and recorded messages reflected the goodness, love, and selflessness of those who faced death.

And what do they tell us, in their final phone calls and e-mails to those they loved, if not of the simple goodness of people that preachers mistakenly call sinners and we mistakenly call ordinary? The pain of the 9/11 victims seems fresher than that of the Titanic victims and yet sadness bears no time stamp or expiration date and they now intermingle testifying together to the bonds of human love and the sadness that is sown like wheat into the field of passing time.
Eugene C. Kennedy *Bulletins From the Human Side* April 13, 2012

Kennedy writes in a poetic style but you and I know what it is like to face the mystery of life in its everyday form. We work in hospitals, hospices, and nursing homes where we see patients' vulnerability and fears, as well as their goodness. In our quieter moments, we know that their feelings are not very different from our own. Perhaps we cannot stop thinking about the Titanic and the World Trade Center because we, similar to those who lost their lives so tragically, struggle to focus on what is important in life. They remind us that life is about love and caring for one another.

Someone who is newly diagnosed with cancer, an elderly person who is unable to care for herself, or a man who is too fearful to schedule an appointment with a physician are all patients yearning for a caregiver who is sensitive to their deepest needs. When we think about those who lost their lives on the Titanic or in the Trade Center bombings, we can remind ourselves of the important role we are playing right now in the lives of those who may be experiencing a similar panic and who are entrusted to our care.

I will be sensitive to the inner needs of the patients who cross my path today. I'll treat them as I'd like to be treated, and feel gratitude that I'm in a position to help heal the inner and outer needs of others. ♥

A Reflection

Needed: A Spark to Get Going

Have you ever had the experience of needing a spark to get going? I needed one to begin writing this reflection. For some reason I just couldn't get going. I wrote a letter, read the last few pages of a book I wanted to finish, made a phone call, checked emails, and put the finishing touches on the outline of a presentation I'm making next month at an upper Midwest hospital. I did everything except what I needed to do, that is, write this short message due at the publisher tomorrow morning.

Why do we put off what we really want to do—do everything but that one thing we really need to do—while continuing to fret about not being able to get started? I've a guess that goes way back to the time I taught chemistry. I recall demonstrating to wide-eyed students how two elements or compounds, hydrogen and oxygen, could be mixed together in a container with no noticeable results. However, if a spark was provided—a little extra energy—the two elements of hydrogen and oxygen would unite, energy would be released in the form of a little explosion, and they would turn into a new compound, water. Clearly, they needed a spark to ignite them. The demonstration was an effort to explain what chemists call the "energy of activation."

While I cannot vouch for any scientific connection between my inability to get started and the laws of chemistry, I do not think it's much of a reach to say that sparks are indeed what get us going. Electrical sparks in a lab are one thing, having our hearts touched as providers of care is equally effective and no less necessary. I know what got me writing. It was the memory of a saying by Dr. Osler, "We are here to add what we can to life, not to get what we can from life." That was just enough to get me going!

What sparks you?

Was it the sight of a vulnerable patient who needs your care? Was it a walk in the woods or a particularly refreshing vacation? Did you remember something about why you chose your profession?

When we put off what we need to do, we need a spark. Deadlines and duty sometimes get us going. However, sparks that touch the heart are immensely more effective.

Elisabeth Kübler-Ross thought that caregivers are sparked by what lies deep within their hearts. In her words:

> *Learn to get in touch with silence within yourself*
> *and know that everything in this life has a purpose.*
> *There are no mistakes, no coincidences.*
> *All events are blessings given to us to learn from.*

Is your heart open to being touched?

What sparks me into action? If I'm procrastinating, I'll examine the source of my delay and see if I can set in motion an event that will generate new energy in me. By learning more about what energizes me, I will know how to re-engage in my life and work. ♥

A Reflection

During dinner with a particularly young looking vibrant grandmother, the conversation turned to her grandchildren, as you might expect. Knowing that I am involved in health care and notwithstanding frequent comments on how bad hospital care is, she wanted to assure me that her family was appreciative of the way her triplet grandchildren found their way into this world almost six years ago. "You can't imagine the joy of knowing that their mother was safe and what it was like to see those little creatures in the NICU. They were preemies, around four pounds each. I leaned over and kissed two of them but before I could get to the third baby they told me to stop. I wasn't supposed to touch them. What grandmother could resist? I couldn't help myself." I thought to myself, I bet those nurses had their hands full with the affection and outgoing ways of this grandmother!

That got me thinking. Those infants, now kids doing well today, were born into a world where they were wanted and cherished. So great were they wanted, that their parents used IVF techniques to conceive. As the years pass, the kids will awaken to the love of their parents. They will not likely become aware of the little village of caregivers who made their birth possible as well as safe. If I could speak with those children I would name some of the villagers.

First, there were the nurses. Their love was not as effusive as grandma's, but every bit as necessary. They were the ones who insured the babies' warmth, watched the monitors, and— among other duties—kept an eye out for apnea, and noted their Ca, K, glucose, phosphate, and bilirubin levels.

There is little need to mention the physicians as part of the village. What mother, particularly those with high-risk pregnancies, does not have a particularly unique and trusting relationship with her caregiver? I've seen a physician who has delivered over 1,200 babies cry following the successful birth of an infant to a woman who feared that her child would be stillborn.

I would also mention the twenty or so technicians who work in the IVF lab. If they had not done their job well, there would be no children.

Neither would the birth of the infants have even happened without the work of a twelve member medical ethics committee that struggled with the seemingly esoteric question of how many fertilized eggs the physicians should allow to develop. Would it not be more ethical and prudent to allow just one, rather than three? Those ethicists, equally caring and wanting what was best for the mother and her children, are surely part of the caring village.

And then there are those who are almost unnoticed as they go about expressing their care by painting, warming, cooling, cleaning and repairing the facilities. Their number is legion. It may surprise many to learn that these caregivers outnumber those we usually call "caregivers" by a margin of three to one.

Did I mention the managers and administrators? Without their contribution, there would be no NICU. And on it goes.

Why do I mention the village and its people? Because most of us—given the pace of life and our responsibilities—seldom have time to think about the value of what we do. We may not express our love as grandmothers do yet we surely love.

I'll be aware of those who care for patients beyond the professions we typically consider "caregivers" and I'll appreciate their contribution. Caregivers include family members, transporters, facilities workers, and billing and janitorial staff. I'll express my gratitude to these often unseen and unappreciated givers of care. ❦

A Reflection

BEING BORED

Whatever our job, now and again we get bored. During an off campus retreat, one of the participants said that she got sleepy every time she sat down at her computer to complete performance evaluations. "Just thinking about the need to get them done makes me tired."

A highly respected physician told me that she avoids the dullness resulting from seeing one patient after another in the same office day after day by skipping lunch. Instead of going to the physician's lounge for a bite to eat, she takes unscheduled 15 minute breaks four or five times a day. "As soon as I yawn I take it as a sign to disappear for ten or fifteen minutes. Sometimes I close my eyes. When the weather is good I walk outside. It is amazing how helpful those breaks are."

Many of us may not have the freedom to take a small break when we start to feel bored. When I'm feeling dull, weary, tired or sleepy, I tend to fall into the trap of grabbing something to munch or drink. I admit that my way of handling boredom is not as effective as the physician's.

Last night I had the good fortune to hear the poet laureate, W.S. Merwin, read some of his poems. During the discussion period that followed, he reflected on his experience of gardening. First, he said—and I paraphrase—have you ever thought when you walk among the foliage you are in a place where every plant and every bug knows more than you do? That little seed you hold in your hand, knows how to grow. The odd-looking, curious bug crawling unseen under the rock knows what he is to do. As much as you may know about gardening you are the learner among those who know. You are the one to be taught.

As he spoke, my thoughts drifted back to work. What would happen if we brought that degree of humility, inquisitiveness, and respect to work?

The curious fact is that Merwin is not only one of our country's esteemed poets, he is also said to have cultivated one of the most beautiful gardens at his home on Maui. Do you think that his stance as a learner influences how he lives and even contributes to the quality of his poetry and gardening? I bet they do. I would also wager that developing that attitude is a sure way to avoid boredom.

Patients come to us seeking help. They rely on our knowledge and expertise. Yet suppose we thought of ourselves as gardeners, walking about where others know so much more than we. Would patient care suffer or would it be enhanced?

While Merwin is a poet and gardener, it seems to me that he is teaching us something important about employment. Whether we work at the bedside, mine data, work as patient advocates, or manage large departments—if we approach our responsibilities as learners, not only will our work be enhanced, we will not likely become bored.

While humility is out of favor these days, it is not all bad; it leaves us open to new ideas and solutions. Discovery of what patients feel and think is a sure remedy for boredom and an ingredient of good patient care.

I'll be open to new views and new ways of doing things. By admitting I don't know it all, I not only learn more, but become energized in the process. To learn is to be engaged, an antidote to boredom and prescription for better patient care. ♥

A Reflection

I'm Me. I'm also Vulnerable

These days, all of us are mindful of the importance of double or even triple checking the identity of those receiving care. Asking for names, checking arm bracelets, and making doubly sure we have the correct medical charts have all become established practices. Who has not heard the horror stories of situations where patients have been injured because of misidentification?

Yesterday I became keenly aware of the critical importance of this issue in an unusual way. While driving on the Interstate my cell phone rang. My wife was driving and I answered the call. It was a credit card company calling to ask if I had purchased several hundred dollars of electronic equipment earlier in the day at a store in New York. "No," I said, "I'm in New Mexico." "I thought so," she countered. "Someone has forged a credit card with your name, address and account number, and is using it in New York." I was shocked since my cards were in my wallet.

The fact that the credit card company discovered the theft so quickly, could change my account number immediately, and have a new credit card to me by noon the next day was amazing. What was not so positive was the fear, anxiety, and concerns that flooded over me. I felt helpless. How did someone get my personal information? What else did they know about me? Do they have my bank account numbers? Is my wife safe? Am I safe? What will this do to our credit scores given the fact that we are in the process of refinancing our home? You name it, I worried about it.

What does all of this have to do with the way we care for our patients and one another? In many ways, everything. While patients have not had their credit card information stolen, they almost always feel vulnerable and exposed if for no other reason than an illness or condition has overtaken them. Most feel as if they have little control over what is happening to them.

What could be more unsettling? The moment a woman feels a lump in her breast, or a man awakens in the ED after a near fatal accident, both know how life grows dearer, and they grow more vulnerable, all in an instant. That is the experience of every patient with a critical illness.

Having my credit card stolen is one thing; facing serious illness is another. However, maybe knowing how vulnerable I felt yesterday will help me be a better caregiver today. Given the rush and demands of the day, what helps you bring a healing presence to patients?

I'll reflect on the vulnerability my patients are experiencing today. I will tap into an experience I've had where I've felt out of control. With greater awareness, empathy grows and so does my ability to be a healing presence. ♥

A Reflection

Three employees who usually meet for lunch were sitting at a table in the corner of the cafeteria. One was a librarian, the second was a nurse who was the director of the hospital's medical research department and the third was a retired physician who often frequented the cafeteria after attending the weekly Continuing Medical Education lecture. I was part of their conversation by chance.

It seems all three knew a former employee who was previously an executive assistant in the hospital's residency program. Evidently the assistant had recently left employment at the hospital to take a position at the state's prestigious University Medical Center where she had landed the job of coordinating their continuing education program. The retired physician thought she was the wrong choice for the job. "She's a good executive assistant but she doesn't know anything about coordinating medical education. They'll soon find out!"

The librarian was quiet and didn't say anything other than, "I'm happy for her. It's a big step up and I bet she does well."

The nurse was anything but quiet. She was delighted that the woman made the jump to the new responsibilities and seemed to take umbrage with the physician's opinion. As best as I can remember, her words were:

"I admire that woman. She embodies that old adage 'be more than you can be.' That's what most people are afraid to do. I think that the only way we grow is to test our limits. I tell my kids 'you can be anything you want to be.' I know damn well that's not entirely true. They have limits but the only way they'll discover them is to reach out and try. So what if she can't do the job. She will have learned something about herself and her talents. My hunch is she'll succeed. I wouldn't be surprised if she goes on to some other job from there."

What was interesting to me was the fact that the retired physician sat there for a minute, then smiled, and said, "Thanks." During the conversation that followed, he mentioned that the only regret in his professional life was the fact that he did not put his hat in the ring to become president of the medical staff when the position opened up three years before his retirement. "I thought I might not be a good one and I didn't want to retire on a bad note!"

As we were leaving, the librarian who spoke little during much of the table talk turned toward the physician and said in a pleasant way, "Neither you, the staff, the patients, nor the hospital have profited by your hesitancies."

I left the table in a reflective mood. Goethe's thought came to mind. "If I accept you as you are, I will make you worse; however if I treat you as though you are what you are capable of becoming, I help you become that." I wonder how many of us settle for less than we can be.

I will reflect on my career and life choices. Have I settled for less or taken risks to fulfill my life and work's purpose? Next time I'm faced with the choice, I'll take the risk to exceed my wildest expectations. ♥

A Reflection

Last week Oprah Winfrey ended a 25-year stint as host of her highly popular afternoon TV show. Amidst much hype and a media blitz, thousands of her fans gathered in Chicago to bid farewell, thank her for her leadership and acknowledge the contribution she has made in their lives.

Whatever you think of Oprah, she has been the source of inspiration for women seeking to find their voice, has effectively furthered the need and value of reading among adults, has contributed millions of dollars to improve the education of children both here and abroad, and most importantly, has modeled an ability to openly and respectfully discuss sensitive issues. In many ways, no topic was off limits—whether too hot to touch or too controversial to address.

Commenting on Oprah's contribution, a highly regarded chaplain who has worked for years within hospital and hospice settings said, "She accomplished what the churches have not been able to accomplish. People listen to her, they take her advice, she awakens within them a sense of hope as well as of power, and she is not afraid to speak of spirituality in a meaningful way."

Personally, I have traveled the world too many times and seen what churches have accomplished—largely by women of faith—to alleviate poverty and improve the health of the world's poor, to imply that they have been ineffective. Yet I think the chaplain has a point. She is reminding us how one person—savvy of the contemporary scene and aware of societal needs—has the zeal to make a significant difference in many peoples' lives. That is something all of us need to notice and follow.

How often, within our differing health care settings, does it seem as if we are powerless to make much of a difference in the lives of others? How often do we pull back when we need to step up to a leadership role? How often have we remained silent when we have had something to say?

Looking back over the years, we know how towering individuals have changed the course of history and the way we care for others. We have the Florence Nightingales of nursing, the bedside teachings of Doctor William Osler, and the example of Mother Teresa to reiterate the value of hard work combined with simply being present to those who are suffering. Maybe this is the time that all of us, no matter how small or inconsequential we may feel, need to try to make a difference in whatever health care setting we serve.

"We're all called. If you're here breathing, you have a contribution to make to our human community. The real work of your life is to figure out your function—your part in the whole—as soon as possible, and then get about the business of fulfilling it as only you can." —Oprah Winfrey

I can't control other people, but I can control myself. I will direct my actions, thoughts and intentions to create the highest good. I'll take risks and take comfort knowing that I'm living my life to the fullest. ♡

A Reflection

When the "Arab Spring" uprising occurred in Egypt, the world watched with interest, concern, excitement, and fear. How amazing it was to know that hundreds of thousands of people were linked real time by the Internet and that we could observe what was occurring on the streets of Cairo as it happened. Amazing, too, is the realization that the distance between a leader and the populace can become so great that a massive uprising is spawned.

Perhaps the realization should not be shocking. Many of us recall hearing the difference between effective and ineffective leaders. Effective leaders look over their shoulders and find a throng of followers. Ineffective leaders look back and see no one. I recall hearing a nurse-manager say something similar. She said that her rule of thumb was "anyone can tell people what to do and then check up on them. I want to show my team where we have to go and then marvel at how well they get there."

None of us are world leaders and most of us are not administrators, directors or managers. Nevertheless, we are leaders insofar as we influence others as we go about our work, whatever our responsibilities might be. No one needs to be reminded of how we influence others if they've experienced first hand how a CEO can influence the culture of a hospital or how a single individual can change the tone of an office, team, or unit. Each of us, by the way we are present as we work, has a remarkable influence. The question is, do we realize the effect we have on others?

To glimpse our influence all we need to do is look back over our lives. Chances are that you and I remember how a parent, aunt, spouse, teacher, neighbor, friend, child, boss or colleague has influenced us in favorable or negative ways. Others remember us similarly.

Why is it so easy to forget our influence? One reason may be that we feel we are only ordinary folks. Some world leaders may not think of themselves as ordinary and lacking in influence but many of us do. I bet you have not found many caregivers wanting to stand apart or proclaim themselves outstanding, exceptional, gifted, or remarkable individuals.

Yet maybe you and I are special as well as influential. Wasn't it Viktor Frankl who, after being imprisoned and stripped of his dignity, family, and all earthly possessions in the holocaust, awakened to the realization that neither his life nor anyone else's is repeatable or replaceable? He believed that each of us has a dignity as well as a unique calling that only we can fulfill. In his words, a life unlived will not be lived by another.

If you've time, take a moment to think about how your presence at work influences others. I would not be surprised if you return to work with a renewed sense of well-being and a heightened appreciation for your calling.

"Do not go where the path may lead; go instead where there is no path and leave a trail."—Ralph Waldo Emerson

I'll look for opportunities to lead today. I can have a profound and positive influence on one person that will last a lifetime. It may start with smile, holding a hand, or reassuringly touching a shoulder. ♡

A Reflection

When Steve Jobs died, his passing was the topic on all the media outlets. Newspapers ran editorials and TV news reports catalogued his remarkable accomplishments. It is easy to see why. Who has not heard about or used an iPhone, iPad, iTV, iPod, or iMac? I marvel every time I get on a plane, settle into my seat, and bring out my favorite piece of technology— a minuscule one inch by one inch by 1/8th inch iPod that holds enough music to nurture my spirit however long the trip. A few years ago, who would have believed that we could carry the works of Beethoven, the Beatles, Mozart, and Willie Nelson around on a chip and access those masterpieces whenever we wanted? Steve Jobs played a major role in making this possible. Investors in Apple are surely appreciative.

While the media praises his business acumen, it seems that Mr. Jobs viewed his accomplishments differently from his admirers. When Dr. Ornish, his physician and confidant, asked Steve Jobs if he were glad that he had kids—given the pace of his life, the demands of the workplace, and his desire to excel—Mr. Jobs' response may seem surprising. *The New York Times* reported him to have said, "[Having kids] is 10,000 times better than anything I've ever done." Clearly, for this man who knew his days were numbered, founding a company, amassing a financial fortune, and creating new products paled when compared to having children. How did he spend his last days? Were they at the office? No, they were at home with his wife and children, away from the business world.

Steve Jobs had his critics. Many bristled at the way he protected his privacy and resented his seemingly authoritarian ways. They found him something of a mystery man who held his cards close to his chest and followed the beat of his own drum.

I have a different slant. I think his lifestyle and ways reflected someone who valued, nourished and protected an inward life.

By "inward" I refer, in part, to an imaginative world that transcends the world that is, and looks toward what may be. Just as it takes a creative mind to develop new products, it takes equally creative caregivers to understand and respond to the experience and needs of patients. It was the best selling author of the Harry Potter series, J.K. Rowling who noted the connection between imagination and care. "Imagination is not only the uniquely human capacity to envision that which is not, and therefore, the foundation of all invention and innovation. It is [also] the power that enables us to empathize with humans whose experiences we have never shared."

Whether we work at the bedside of patients or support those who do, it is easy to be dulled by our responsibilities and to lose sight of our inward lives. Who has not felt the heaviness of daily obligations, the need to respond to the real needs of successive patients, the day-to-day sameness of things, the challenge of working with others when disagreements arise, the periodic waning of our energies or any number of other challenges? Without an inward life work can become a series of responsibilities robbed of their value. Steve Jobs' life is a reminder that as important as our work is, it is equally valuable to think about, and to nourish, our lives apart from work. The two are connected.

I will honor my inward life. It is vibrant with ideas and new perspective. My commitment to myself is to be quiet, turn inward and listen. ♥

A Reflection

PERSPECTIVE

Has anyone not felt bent out of shape by the words or behavior of a colleague, actions of a manager, or the feeling that the Administrator does not really understand the needs of those who work with patients? It is amazing how conflicts, whether real or imagined, can sour how we feel about others, our work, and even the nursing home, hospital or office where we work.

Even more striking is the way we are sometimes buoyed by a vacation, a conversation with a trusted friend, or learning something new about a person or situation that had troubled us but now has changed how we feel. "I had no idea that was the case." "I thought he did it because he was angry at me." "I didn't know that…"

I realized that the perspective we bring to a situation influences what we see when I had coffee with a highly creative and successful colleague whom I had not seen in years. We became friends when we worked at the same hospital. One of the directors was a gruff fellow intent on making changes to improve the quality of patient care and his department's financial performance. His intentions were good but his style left something to be desired. My friend felt that his style was abusive. She looked for another job, found one across town, and jumped.

She told me that she loved her new setting. "It's amazing," she said, "that working in a hospital just 15 miles away from the other is so different." When I asked how they were different, without a moment's hesitation she added, "I see things differently from the time we worked together. When I was working with you the director bugged me to no end. I thought he was a jerk. I couldn't wait to get out of there. Now that I'm here I can see that I didn't know how to be honest with him. Instead of speaking up, I was so miffed by the way he did things that

I didn't say anything. In this hospital I've learned that if I speak up—even if I complain about something—nobody falls apart and the world doesn't end. If I had known that years ago, I bet I'd still work over there."

I wondered how she learned to morph from a person who was pleasant and quiet to one who had found her voice. Thinking that it must have had something to do with her new director's style, or maybe that she had received effective psychotherapy, I asked how she had made the change. I was surprised by her response.

"Have you ever looked up on a clear night and noticed the stars? I mean really looked up. That is when it came to me in a way I had never experienced before. This earth of ours is infinitesimally small and the universe is unfathomably immense. And I mean unfathomably. Have you seen the recent photographs from the Hubble Telescope? They put work and life's frustrations as well as its joys, in perspective. They also put me in perspective. I can't tell you how that thought has changed the way I live, including how I work." After a minute she added, "You look like you don't believe me."

Honestly, I did believe her. My puzzled look was because of the simplicity of her answer. Our perspective—what we see and consequently what we think—markedly influences how we live. I bet her patients benefit from her newly found perspective. I know that she has. I've been left to think about my perspective.

I'll devote time today to reflect on what's important in my life. I'll consider how my actions and presence can reflect a new attitude where I put life's trials and disappointments in proper perspective and remember what I value. ♥

A Reflection

WHAT DOES IT MEAN TO BE HEALTHY?

This week I was on a conference call with a group of hospital leaders concerned with how to improve the health of their community. They felt they were providing excellent clinical services to those who were acutely ill, but wondered if it was not also their responsibility to improve the general health status of their community. Oddly, they were concerned because they'd just learned that their community represented one of the healthiest cities in which to live as reported by the Center for Disease and Control's "Healthy People 2020" initiative. Should they rest on their laurels and continue to do things as they have or should they try to improve?

After considerable discussion, they concluded that their medical center had a responsibility to partner with other organizations to improve the health of their community and that it was short sighted of them to think that their role was limited to caring for the acutely ill. I was pleased and surprised by their decision. It has significant program and monetary implications.

That surprise, however, was minimal when compared to the challenge that an oncology clinical nurse specialist raised on the conference call. She asked, seemingly out of the blue, "What does it mean to be healthy?" There was silence on the phone. After a time, one of the participants jumped in. "All you have to do is to look at what has been measured. They've measured a million determinants. Here, I'll read them to you." He then mentioned, obesity, chronic illnesses, smoking, infant birth weight, teen pregnancy, death rates, immunizations, asthma, sexually transmitted diseases, physical activity, availability of primary care, suicide, and addictions.

Again, there was quiet on the phone. That is when the nurse jumped back in with the remark, "That's my point. They are all measures of physical health. I don't think the researchers have ever worked with real patients. I've had many critically ill patients who are as healthy as can be. They may be broken in body but not in mind and spirit. I'm all in favor of improving the health status of our community but I think we should broaden the way we think of health."

Her challenge and outspoken manner has me wondering. I cannot stop thinking about her statement, "I've had many critically ill patients who are as healthy as can be." I think she has a point. The problem is how to measure that kind of health? Perhaps we cannot and need not. It was Einstein who reminded us on several occasions that, "Not everything that can be counted counts, and not everything that counts can be counted."

I do not think anyone would question the value of doing all that we can to control obesity, decrease the prevalence of chronic illness, curtail smoking, provide prenatal care for moms, immunizations for all children, and reduce addictive behaviors. While we need to continue to work at improving our physical health, we also need to be attentive to those activities that nourish the mind and heart if we are to improve the health of our communities. I am grateful to that nurse who challenged those of us on the conference call to broaden our ways of thinking.

I'll reflect on a broader meaning of "health." Are my body, mind and spirit healthy? I will take action today to nurture my health physically, emotionally, and spiritually. It's a commitment I can make to myself every day. ♥

Notes ⇝

References

Introduction

1. Kierkegaard, Soren. 1843. Two Edifying Discourses. quoted in Robert Bretall (editor). 1946. A Kierkegaard Anthology. Princeton: Princeton University Press. p.108.

2. Cook, E.T. the Life of Florence Nightengale, 1820-1861. (1913) p. 1, p. 237 (available Google Digital Library)

3. Billie Holiday quotes. April 1, 2012 "ThinkExist.com Quotations Online

Chapter 1

1. Whyte, D. 2009. The Three Marriages: Reimagining Work, Self and Relation ship. New York: Riverhead Books.

2. Moore, T. 2008. A Life at Work: The Joy of Discovering What You Were Born to Do. Portland, OR: Broadway Books.

3. Frankl, V. E. 2006. Man's Search for Meaning. Boston: Beacon Press.

4. Ibid.

Chapter 2

1a. Dyer, Wayne. 2010. Taking Your Life From Ambition to Meaning. Carlsbad. CA. p. 41.

1. Einstein, A. 1933. On the Method of Theoretical Physics. The Herbert Spencer Lecture. Oxford: Clarendon Press.

2. Whitehead, A. N. 2010. The Concept of Nature: The Tarner Lectures Delivered in Trinity College, November 1919 (1920). Whitefish, MT: Kessinger Publishing.

2a. Chittister, J. The Gift of Years: Growing Older Gracefully. Katonah, NY: Blue Bridge, 2008.

3. Neff, W. S. 2006. Work and Human Behavior. New Brunswick, NJ: Aldine Transaction.

4. Ibid.

5. Friedman, E. H. 2011. Generation to Generation: Family Process in Church and Synagogue. New York: Guilford.

6. Ibid.

7. Neff, Work and Human Behavior.

8. O'Donohue, J. 1997. Anam Cara: A Book of Celtic Wisdom. New York: HarperCollins.

Chapter 3

1a. Erikson, Erik H. 1976. The Power and Limits of a Vision. New York: The Free Press, p. 136.

1. Friedman, M., and R. H. Rosenman. 1982. Type A Behavior and Your Heart. New York: Fawcett.

2. Kamarck, T. 2012. Psychosocial stress and cardiovascular disease: An exposure science perspective. Psychological Science Agenda 26. Available at www.apa.org/science/about/psa/2012/04/stress-cardiovascular.aspx.

3. Woolman, M. 1982. Addiction to Perfection: The Still Unravished Bride. Toronto: Inner City Books.

4. Norris, K. 2008. Acedia & Me: A Marriage, Monks, and a Writer's Life. New York: Riverhead Books.

5. Mounier, Emmanuel. 1923 & 2011. Personalism. London: Routledge and Kegan Paul. P3.

Chapter 4

1a. Campbell, Joseph. 1989. Joseph Campbell in Conversation with Michael Toms. New York: Harper and Row. p. 88.

1. Lewis, C. S. 1960. The Four Loves. New York: Harcourt Brace Jovanovich.

1b. O'Neal, N. The life of St. Ignatius of Loyola. Available at norprov.org/spirituality/lifeofignatius.htm.

2. Ignatius of Loyola. 1548. The Spiritual Exercises, no. 234.

3. Van den Berg, J. H. 1966. The Psychology of the Sickbed. Pittsburgh: Duquesne University Press.

3a. Sears, Benjamin. 2011. Irving Berlin. New York: Oxford University Press. p. 15.

3b. Byrne, John A. July 1, 2005. "The Fast Company Interview: Jeff Immelt." New York: Fast Company. p. 3.

4. Lewis, The Four Loves.

5. O'Donohue, Anam Cara.

6a. "Dali Lama quotes" ThinkExist.com Quotations Online. 2 May. 2012. http://thinkexist.com/quotes/dali_lama/.

6b. Morris, John T. June 11, 2011. Aldea Restaurant. Prepublished lyrics.

7. Jung, C. G. 1976. The Portable Jung. New York: Penguin.

7a. Heck, Kathleen. 2008. After the Beep: A Glimpse at the Wired Workplace. Lincoln, NE. iUniverse. p. 171.

7b. Ashton, Dore. 1972. Picasso on Art: A Selection of Views. New York: Da Capo Press. p. 49.

8. Frankl, Man's Search for Meaning.

Chapter 5

1 Horney, Karen. 1951. Neurosis and Human Growth. London: Routledge and Kegan Paul Ltd. p. 64.

Chapter 7

1. Lynch, J. J. 1977. Broken Heart: The Medical Consequences of Loneliness. New York: Basic Books.

2. Badaracco, J. L. Jr. 1997. Defining Moments: When Managers Must Choose Between Right and Right. Cambridge, MA: Harvard Business School Press.

3. Ibid.

4. Gilot, Francoise. 2005. Life with Picasso. Chicago: Raintree. p. 5.

Chapter 8

1. New York Times. 2010. Monster.com. December 7.

2. Rilke, R. M. 2009. Letters to a Young Poet. Mineola, NY: Dover Publications.

3. Frankl, Man's Search for Meaning

3a. Keen, Sam. 1991. Fire in the Belly: On Being a Man. New York: Bantam. p. 177

3b. Buechner, Frederick. 1992. Listening to Your Life: Daily Meditations with Frederick Buechner. New York: HarperCollins. p. 186.

4. Ibid. (Frankl)

4a. Moore, Thomas. 2008. A Life at Work: The Joy of Discovering What You Were Born to Do. New York: Broadway Books. p. 181.

5. Ibid. (Frankl)

Selected Reading

Aaron, David. *The Secret Life of God: Discovering the Divine Within You.* Boston: Shambhala Publications, 2004. Writing in a conversational style from a uniquely Jewish perspective, Aaron, a rabbi, is well-informed and humorous. His thoughts are particularly challenging when he asserts and explains his belief that each individual has a unique mission—"the ultimate gift from the Ultimate One."

Barkin, Laurie. *The Comfort Garden: Tales from the Trauma Unit.* San Francisco: Fresh Pond Press, 2011. Of particular value in this easy-to-read and honest book about Barkin's extensive nursing experience is the way she has learned to deal with compassion fatigue. Readers who feel overwhelmed and exhausted will gain insight from, and find support and reaffirmation in, nurses' critical need to care for themselves so they can provide high-quality care to patients.

Bateson, Mary Catherine. *Composing a Life.* New York: Penguin Books, 1990. Bateson reflects on the inspirational lives of five extraordinary women, each successful yet grounded in the turbulence of life. She views life as an improvisational art form, with interruptions, conflicted priorities, and demands as a source of wisdom and well-being. This essay clearly illustrates the difference between having a career and the challenge of becoming one's calling.

Brim, Gilbert. *Ambition: How We Manage Success and Failure Throughout Our Lives.* New York: Basic Books, 1992. From the social psychology perspective, Brim blends personal experience and years of research findings to help us understand the need to manage our desire to excel. He describes the roles that success and failure play in managing the goals we set for ourselves.

Brooks, David. *The Social Animal: The Hidden Sources of Love, Character, and Achievement.* New York: Random House, 2011. This book for laymen synthesizes current research regarding how we develop as individuals. According to Brooks, social influences are pivotal forces; on pp. 116–132, he describes how work personality may form during adolescence. The book is stimulating whether you agree or disagree with Brooks's views.

Cain, Susan. *Quiet: The Power of Introverts in a World That Can't Stop Talking.* New York: Crown, 2012. This well-researched, witty, and easy-to-read book is a must for quiet, reflective individuals who feel misplaced in their jobs.

Chittister, Joan. *The Gift of Years: Growing Older Gracefully.* Katonah, NY: Blue-Bridge, 2008. Although Chittister focuses on aging-related issues from the spirituality perspective, she deftly describes the experience of work as a prelude to understanding the gift of aging. She writes for those in their seventies. The book will be an eye-opener for younger persons who know they work in driven ways.

De Botton, Alain. *The Pleasures and Sorrows of Work.* New York: Pantheon Books, 2009. De Botton has an eye for detail and can look at different jobs and professions in creative and imaginative ways. If you've ever wondered why you exhaust yourself when working or what makes work fulfilling or soul-destroying, read De Botton. His prose is artful, his perspective unique.

Delbanco, Nicholas. *Lastingness: The Art of Old Age.* New York: Grand Central Publishing, 2011. A gem of a book by an author who wants to know why some artists' work diminishes with age while that of others reaches a peak as the years pass. Delbanco's exploration hints at what we need to keep our creativity and enthusiasm alive as we mature.

Dossey, Larry. *Space, Time & Medicine.* Boston: Shambhala Publications, 1982. Dossey, a physician, brings a creative and critical eye to the contemporary practice of medicine while advancing a convincing, research-based, contrarian view of what is necessary to heal mind, body, and soul. The chapter "Time and Disease" clearly explains how hurriedness and illness are interrelated. Current studies, including some of the most advanced neurological research, continue to support and clarify views he first expressed 30 years ago.

Dunne, John S. *The Reasons of the Heart: A Journey into Solitude and Back Again into the Human Circle.* New York: Macmillan, 1978. Written from the perspective of spirituality, this book is as timely today as it was nearly 40 years ago. Dunne's reflections require slow reading and a willingness to look inward.

Friedman, Edwin H. *Generation to Generation: Family Process in Church and Synagogue.* New York: Gilford Press, 1985. Friedman's research focuses on the replication of learned family dynamics in church ministries. His book convincingly illustrates the influence of family on the development of the work personality.

Griffin, Emilie. *The Reflective Executive: A Spirituality of Business and Enterprise.* New York: Crossroad Publishing, 1993. The author describes her experience finding God in the workplace. This book is for those who wonder if hospitals, clinics, nursing homes, and physician practices are sacred places.

Guiliano, Mireille. *Women, Work & the Art of Savoir Faire: Business Sense & Sensibility.* New York: Atria Books, 2009. This conversational-style book was written for and about women. Guiliano, a highly successful former CEO of Clicquot Inc., describes what she has discovered—and what she believes every woman will need to discover—to be successful in the business world, one that's only open to a few. Her thoughts, world view, and assumptions are provocative.

Jaques, Elliott. *Requisite Organization: A Total System for Effective Managerial Organization and Managerial Leadership for the 21st Century.* Arlington, VA: Cason Hall & Co., 1988. This how-to manual is a must read for CEOs and senior executives who need to understand, and embark on a journey to transform, their organization. For those who aspire to leadership positions in health care, it clearly outlines and describes the competencies they will need. Individuals already in leadership positions who lack these competencies will recognize how executives may become work addicted, work fixated, or work exhausted.

Koloroutis, Mary, ed. *Relationship-Based Care: A Model for Transforming Practice.* Minneapolis: Creative Health Care Management, 2004. Written by experienced nurses, this creative, practical, and comprehensive outline of nursing practice addresses the need to establish a caring, healing, professional practice in hospitals to ensure the primacy of patient care and the health of caregivers. It received the Book of the Year Award from the American Journal of Nursing.

Kugel, James L. *In the Valley of the Shadow: On the Foundations of Religious Belief.* New York: Free Press, 2011. When Kugel, a Harvard professor, was diagnosed with an aggressive form of cancer, the music of daily life stopped and "there you are, one little person, sitting in the late summer sun, with only a few things left to do." His perspective reveals a world "that opens onto a stark, new landscape ordinarily hidden from human eyes."

Lynch, James J. 2000. *A Cry Unheard: New Insights into the Medical Consequences of Loneliness.* Baltimore, MD: Bancroft Press. This readable and challenging book catalogues research studies documenting the link between health and human dialogue. Lynch coins the phrase "communicative disease" to note the problems that rise when lack of human contact leads to an isolation with medical consequences.

Lowman, Rodney L. *The Clinical Practice of Career Assessment: Interests, Abilities, and Personality.* Washington, DC: American Psychological Association, 1991. Although written for clinicians who assess individuals regarding their career choice, Lowman's book illustrates the complex interplay of forces that are operating when people try to find the "right job."

Maslach, Christina. *Burnout: The Cost of Caring.* Englewood Cliffs, NJ: Prentice Hall, 1982. Maslach's words for nurses, counselors, teachers, police officers, social workers, and caregivers of every stripe have withstood the test of time. This book is a quick read that generates lasting insights. Maslach also co-edited *Professional Burnout: Recent Developments in Theory and Research* (Washington, DC: Taylor & Francis, 1993), an academic approach to the topic, and co-authored *The Truth About Burnout: How Organizations Cause Personal Stress and What to Do About It* (San Francisco: Jossey-Bass, 1997).

Moore, Thomas. *A Life at Work: The Joy of Discovering What You Were Born to Do.* Portland, OR.: Broadway Books, 2008. This reflective essay is perhaps the clearest and most understandable description of the interplay between work and life. If you only have time to read one book this year, this should be it. You will likely be awakened, challenged, and affirmed.

Nhat Hanh, Thich. *Peace is Every Breath.* New York: HarperCollins, 2011. In a straightforward, practical manner, Thich Nhat Hanh makes the core teachings of Buddha understandable and accessible to those interested in living a balanced life in the world rather than withdrawn from it. This is gem of a book by the famous Zen Master.

Palmer, Parker J. *A Hidden Wholeness: The Journey Toward an Undivided Life.* San Francisco: Jossey-Bass, 2004. The jacket accurately describes Palmer's book, written from a spiritual perspective: "At a time when many of us seek ways of working and living that are more resonant with our souls, *A Hidden Wholeness* offers insight into our condition and guidance for finding what we seek within ourselves and with each other."

Payne, Roy, and Jenny Firth-Cozens, eds. *Stress in Health Professionals.* New York: John Wiley & Sons, 1987. The essays in this book, one of many in a Wiley series on occupational stress, describe the stresses associated specifically with medical training and general practice, and experienced by women physicians, surgeons, psychiatrists, dentists, nurses, and numerous allied health professionals. The text is a helpful reference for those who seek to understand the diverse challenges that health care providers face as they strive to live balanced lives while engaging in demanding professions.

Progoff, Ira. *At a Journal Workshop: Writing to Access the Power of the Unconscious and Evoke Creative Ability.* New York: Penguin Putnam, 1992. This classic is for anyone interested in how using a journal can awaken their inner life. Progoff's reflections on how the human psyche works are also rewarding. The book is out of print, but used copies are available in bookstores and on the Web.

Scarf, Maggie. *September Songs: The Good News About Marriage in the Later Years.* New York: Riverhead Books, 2008. This well-known journalist's gift is an ability to translate psychological and sociological studies into everyday language so readers can understand shared human experiences.

Shulevitz, Judith. *The Sabbath World: Glimpses of a Different Order of Time.* New York: Random House, 2010. This well-researched, reflective, and creative essay, impeccably written from the perspective of Jewish history and spirituality, makes for challenging and delightful reading. Two chapters— "The Scandal of the Holy" and "Time Sickness"— provide different yet complementary views on issues the book addresses.

Vaillant, George E. *Aging Well: Surprising Guideposts to a Happier Life from the Landmark Harvard Study of Adult Development.* New York: Little, Brown and Company, 2002. Read this book if you're concerned about aging as it relates to our work lives. Vaillant, a physician, makes down-to-earth and surprising suggestions.

Van den Berg, J.H. *The Psychology of the Sickbed.* Pittsburgh: Duquesne University Press, 1966. Using a phenomenology approach, Van den Berg describes the near universal experience of illness from the patient perspective. The text is dated, but his descriptions are classic

Whyte, David. *The Three Marriages: Reimagining Work, Self and Relationship.* New York: Riverhead Books, 2009. This is a creative, reflective, and poetic yet practical essay on thinking about our three core relationships—with work, ourselves, and loved ones—as three marriages. Whyte's insights are challenging.

Acknowledgments

Over the last three years, I was fortunate to have three experiences that shaped the way I write about work. Wasn't it Einstein who said tongue-in-cheek that the secret to creativity is to know how to hide your sources? Being a little contrarian, I don't want to hide them. There are three.

The first was an invitation from Brother Vincent Pelletier to speak at the Sangre de Cristo Center in Santa Fe, NM., on the topic of work. Twice a year, about three dozen men and woman from around the world gather there for 100 days of reflection. Each participant is a professional. Each is a religious sister, brother, or priest. They, like many physicians and nurses, experience their lives and work as a calling. What I learned in that setting in the last two years has influenced almost every page of this book. My regret is that I don't have the talent to adequately capture the wisdom of those men and women. The writing herein represents my best effort.

The second experience was my long overdue discovery of Creative Health Care Management. CHCM, one of the oldest nurse-based consulting groups, consists of a highly innovative team of nurse consultants whose mission is to renew and re-ignite health care professionals' spirit of caring. They do that by helping hospitals implement a relationship-based care model.

My ties with CHCM began when I met Marie Manthey, its president emeritus, and Mary Koloroutis, one of its vice presidents. They are truly insightful and committed professionals. I had the good fortune to work with these CHCM experts, all gifted nurses: Colleen Person, Mourine Evans, Mary Pat Thomas, Mary Griffin Strom, Susan Wessell, Janet Weaver, and Suzanne Cleere. They are mentors to hundreds of caregivers and were an inspiration and source of insight for me as I wrote this book.

The third experience was my interactions with many employees at Exempla Health care, an outstanding, Colorado-based system of hospitals, physicians, and clinics that provide the best possible clinical care. It was my privilege for almost 10 years to be its senior vice president for mission. In that position, I had the good fortune to develop a number of personal relationships with employees at all levels. Learning from them is a gift I still cherish. Their lives are reflected in this book. To Jeff Selberg, who was President and CEO of Exempla Healthcare at the time, thank you.

As you will discover on these pages, I am an educator at heart and an author by accident and dint of hard work. I write as a result of having learned something about working in healthy ways, and want to share that knowledge with others.

There is only one reason this book has seen the light of day. It is Terri Moss. Her commitment to improving the quality of patient care underlies her various activities as a publisher, editor, writer, and presenter. I am indebted to her and want to express my gratitude for the gift that she is in my life.

About the Author

Dr. Martin C. Helldorfer writes from a unique perspective. Martin was a monk (De La Salle Brothers) for thirty years, and is a clinical psychologist. His background is rich as well as unique; his words both challenging and affirming.

Before embarking on his current career as a consultant to health care leaders, Martin worked for Exempla Healthcare, a Colorado-based regional health care system, where he held the position of the Senior Vice President for Mission for eight years. Prior to joining Exempla, he served in similar positions in other regional and national health care systems.

Martin knows health care organizations from the inside. His experience on various non-profit boards and his many years of working with employees within hospitals, clinics and out patient settings is extensive. His twenty years of working as a psychologist within two specialized psychiatric treatment centers has also shaped his thought in significant ways.

Healing with Heart: Inspirations for Health Care Professionals won the American Journal of Nursing's Book of the Year Award in the Leadership and Management category and is in its eighth printing. He is also the author of the popular book, *Prayer: A Relationship without Words.* His two previous books, *The Work Trap,* and *Prayer, A Guide When Troubled,* were in continuous print for fifteen years.

Dr. Helldorfer holds a Doctorate in Ministry (psychology) from Andover Newton Theological, and Masters Degrees in chemistry (Notre Dame University), religion and personality (Duquesne University) and theology (La Salle University).

Currently, Martin speaks at health care retreats for both large and small health care systems, leads management retreats, organizes workshops and consults. He lives with his wife in Santa Fe, New Mexico.

About Moss Communications

Terri Moss *Moss Communications* has sustained a long-held mission and vision to create practical, everyday work tools that engage employees to achieve a renewed attitude for their work; one that leaves them inspired and personally fulfilled.

Moss Communications began in 1993 as a boutique consulting firm specializing in employee communications. In 2006, Terri reinvented Moss Communications, forming an independent publishing house and expanding its mission to include publishing books and tools that encourage fuller employee engagement and improved quality of life in the work place.

Through her work, experience as a hospital volunteer, and many hospitalizations as a child, Terri developed a deep and unique sensitivity to the particular challenges and environment in which health care professional work—from a patient's and volunteer's perspective.

Moss Communications' first publication, *Healing with Heart: Inspirations for Health Care Professionals* is in its eighth printing and was awarded the American Journal of Nursing's Book of the

Year in the Leadership and Management category. In addition to *Healing with Heart*, Moss Communications offers these tools to support and encourage deeper human connections among health care professionals:

- Healing with Heart Wisdom Cards
- Healing with Heart Workshops
- *Prayer: A Relationship without Words*
- Healthy Ways to Work in Health Care Workshops

Her inspiration to publish *Healthy Ways to Work in Health Care* and other publications comes from her deep commitment to and appreciation for the importance of clear communication among staff and volunteers throughout an organization, and the critical importance of delivering care with mindfulness and a heart-felt human connection.

She is grateful for meeting Martin Helldorfer, whose inspirational writings allow her to achieve her vision and mission. Working with Martin continues to be a source of great fulfillment and joy.

Terri has been an avid and devoted meditator for over 36 years. She and her family live in the San Francisco Bay Area. She can be reached at terri@mosscommunications.net.

Notes

Notes ～

Notes

Notes ⌁

Notes

Notes

Notes ~

Ordering Information

For information about engaging Martin Helldorfer for speaking, workshops, retreats, and leadership development programs, please contact:
Terri@mosscommunications.net

www.mosscommunications.net

To order *Healing with Heart: Inspirations for Health Care Professionals*, the book, and Wisdom Cards, or the book, *Prayer: A Relationship without Words*, contact Moss Communications. You may purchase using our website's secure online store, or by phone.

Terri@mosscommunications.net

www.mosscommunications.net

phone: 925-377-5288

Discounts are available
for group purchases.